AMBLE AND DISTRICT

AMBLE AND DISTRICT

BY
T. L. McANDREWS

SANDHILL
PRESS

Originally published about 1912 by W.G. Chambers,
16-18 Queen St., Amble and printed at the Northumberland Press,
Waterloo House, Thornton Street, Newcastle upon Tyne.

Reprinted in 1996 by Sandhill Press Ltd., 17 Castle Street,
Warkworth, Morpeth, Northumberland, NE65 0UW.

ISBN 0 946098 39 5

Cover illustration: Warkworth Harbour, Northumberland
(Port of Amble).
View showing the harbour entrance and coal shipping staithes. 1889.
With the kind permission of Newcastle upon Tyne City
Libraries & Arts.

Printed in Great Britain by Martins the Printers,
Berwick upon Tweed.

CONTENTS

LIST OF ILLUSTRATIONS
Repositioned from original edition.

7

Publishers Note to 1996 edition

This unique record of the history of Amble and district was written early this century by Thomas Lawrence McAndrews. Born in Coquetdale in 1858, McAndrews first came to Amble in 1881. He was a working miner at Broomhill Colliery, a Justice of the Peace and for 40 years a dedicated local Councillor. Described as an "intelligent and painstaking man", he was elected to the new Amble Urban Council in 1894, and on his retirement in 1934 the following appreciation of his work appeared in the local press:

"Mr. T.L. McAndrews, of Amble, is retiring after 40 years' service on Amble Urban Council.

When the Parish Councils Act of 1894 gave Amble urban status, Mr. McAndrews was one of the first nine councillors to be elected, and he has continued to serve until the present day.

Born in Upper Coquetdale, Mr. McAndrews went to Amble in 1891, and in over a half a century has played no small part in the town's advancement and welfare, and is particularly proud of the Council's housing, water and electricity schemes.

Mr. McAndrews has had many interests. He was the chief promoter of the Amble Club Ltd., and acted as secretary for the first ten years, and his son - Mr. J.L. McAndrews - has served in a similar capacity for the past 18 years. He assisted in the formation of the Amble golf and bowling clubs, started the now well-known Amble sports club and has been chairman of Amble Rifle Club for many years. He was the pioneer of Amble Literary Society to which he has regularly contributed papers.

For 15 years Mr. McAndrews attended science classes and lectures, and is a local authority on the geology and botany of Northumberland. In his spare time he wrote a history, geology and botany of Amble and district.

As chairman of Amble U.D.C. at the outbreak of war he was responsible for the administration of the Lord-Lieutenant's Fund. He was also recruiting officer for an area of 40 square miles, and with no other assistance than that of his wife enlisted over 1600 men and served on 18 different committees."

Thomas McAndrews died on 6th January 1945 aged 87 years at Bede Street in Amble.

INTRODUCTION

IT is in response to the oft-repeated question:
" Is there no history of Amble? " that
these pages are produced.

Like most first attempts there undoubtedly
are many weaknesses for which I apologise,
but I hope this humble effort to supply a long-
felt want will be accepted in the spirit intended
by the writer.

For the old-time history I have been
indebted to Hodgkin's, " History of Northumberland," Mackenzie's, etc., and especially
to the "New History of Northumberland "
(Warkworth Section), to the compilers of
which I offer my sincere thanks.

For the early Amble of the nineteenth
century I have been very much indebted to
Mr James Rutherford, The Wynd, Amble, to
whom I tender my sincere thanks.

Amongst others who have given me
material assistance I might include Mr James

Earnshaw for the harbour, Mr Thomas Tait for Radcliffe, and for Broomhill Mr C. Purvis.

In the geological chapters, by the severely elementary line it will be apparent that it is only intended for the man in the street, and an attempt to induce the younger generation to take an interest in a most interesting subject.

The botany chapter, most carefully prepared, is entirely the work of my mutual friend the late Mr George Waters, but for whose kindly encouragement these pages would not have seen the light of day, and to whose memory I dedicate this unpretentious volume.

T. L. McANDREWS.

AMBLE AND DISTRICT

SITUATED on a rising eminence which bounds the estuary of the River Coquet, with a long stretch of low-lying land on the south, a gentle, rising ascent to the west, culminating in the Framlington Hills, and on the east the North Sea with its broad expanse of eternal blue, bounds the little town of Amble.

A modest, matter-of-fact workaday town, with little claim to the picturesque ; a veritable treeless waste, where the deep green tints of spring or the varying hues of autumn are of little account. Neither are its historical associations of the vivid, interesting type—rather that of an obscure hamlet with the only claims of having lived in the living present, with the full quota of stress and struggle for an existence.

No proud, powerful baron by feats of arms in the battlefield or tourney has thrown a halo of romance round Amble. No marauding borderer has stained its annals with blood-shed, and the entire absence of any connection with troublesome times stamps its past history with the stamp of peace. The little history connected with Amble has doubtless been dwarfed by the intensely interesting chronicles which spread a romantic charm round the sister hamlet.

What Amble loses in scenery and historical associations is in a measure compensated for by pure, bracing air, and the Amble of to-day is in many ways a model town. Dr H. M. Stumbles, Medical Officer of Health gives some proof of this in his Annual Report for 1909.

" I have to report," he says, " that taking matters all round we may congratulate ourselves on having improved our state very materially during the year 1908. We can boast of a very low death-rate, nine per thousand ; the lowest ever recorded since the formation of the Urban District. There is only a shadow of tuberculosis, with not a single death. As a township we have in our favour an unsurpassed water supply, plenty of good, sound, wholesome food, improved housing conditions, abundance of fresh air, a good drainage system, and all the requirements of a good seaside resort."

According to this report it is apparent that

the little town has a fair share of health,
wealth, and prosperity.

Amble is essentially a modern town, with
substantial stone-built houses, and well-made
streets; a population estimated to be nearly
six thousand—a purely industrial community.
With the great development of the local
collieries in the last quarter of the past century the population has increased from 2,016
in 1881, to the present estimated number in
1909. Unfortunately, as regards commercial
progress, the little town is situated a little
beyond the border-line of the great Newcastle
coal field, which practically terminates with
the Hauxley fault; an upheaval of over a
hundred fathoms, running in a straight line
west, a mile south of Amble.

From a purely economic point of view this
is a serious loss, besides considerably limiting
the proportions of the small town, but this,
in a way, is compensated for by having an open
side free from smoke and grime, the natural,
unfailing results of industrial progress.

The town is practically divided into two
portions by the railway station and the Radcliffe wagon-way breaking up the continuity
of the streets. One main street comprised
almost entirely of shops and other business

places is its chief attraction, and from a purely business point of view Amble will compare favourably with other small industrial towns of a like calling. The population consists chiefly of miners who work in the neighbouring collieries. The people, in general, are of a sturdy, independent order, self-reliant and industrious; a large percentage living in their own property.

This, in a measure, explains why Amble, with all the advantages of a seaside resort, has so few holiday visitors. There can be little doubt, however, that if accommodation was provided, not a few would take advantage of the pure, bracing air, the fine stretch of sandy beach, the extensive Links and sand-hills which command a beautiful view of the Coquet Vale, the distant Cheviots, and Simonside's towering escarpments, which form a skyline to a charming, panoramic, rural picture.

The neighbouring lanes too, with a wealth of natural flowers in the summer months, are especially attractive, and there is also the promenade pier, always a great attraction for most people.

Some day, probably, Amble may blossom into a holiday resort, but at the present time everything turns to a purely industrial centre.

THE CELTIC AGE

The earliest history connected with Amble is of ancient British origin. In 1859, a cist or stone coffin containing a perfect skeleton was found near the south pier. This skeleton of the old-time resident was lying on the left side, with the knees drawn up, and a drinking-cup of the period close by. Other coffins in a less perfect condition, some containing fragments of skeletons, others empty, were found, but very little store was put upon this connecting link with the ancient race by the ordinary man over half a century ago.

Twenty-six years later, in 1885, during excavations at the Link Quarry the real grave-yard of the primitive settlers was struck, viz. a large cairn with a number of coffins each containing a skeleton of varying ages—from the child to the adult. Unfortunately a good many of these were disturbed before the news of the find was conveyed to the Antiquarian Society. Eventually the Rev. Mr Greenwell arrived on the scene, and in a paper read before the Antiquarian Society described the discovery.

It appears that on Mr Greenwell's arrival the cairn had been a good deal disturbed, coffins opened, and bones and urns abstracted, but what he did find he described as a cairn forty feet in diameter and five feet high, built of cobble stones from the beach laid upon a thin layer of vegetable mould, and with clayey soil beneath.

The situation was seventy yards from the edge of the sea beach, under a deposit of nine feet of blown sand. The present-day inroads on this particular part of the coast gives the impression that the graveyard of the ancient Briton was much farther inland than its present position indicates. A rather peculiar coincidence might be noted here, viz. that two thousand years later a cemetery was provided within a stone's throw of the place selected by the semi-savage Celt.

After careful observation, Mr Greenwell came to the conclusion that in all, the cairn contained about twenty cists of the usual kind, several deposits of burnt bones, and an un- usually large number of interments in one sepulchral mound. There were several pieces of pottery—one of which he says he found himself. The urns and other implements seem to have been the greatest antiquarian prizes, and some of this savage pottery and other instruments are now in the sacred trust of the British Museum, while others adorn the collection of an Alnwick gentleman; but, unfortunately, not a scrap of this wonderful prehistoric discovery is now in Amble.

At a later period other cists were found containing large urns, at a considerable distance from the cairn.

In the sand cover of the quarry a black streak can be traced almost on a level with these graves, and it does not require a great stretch of imagination to come to the conclusion that this indicates the surface on which the wild man trod, in the far remote ages of the past. About a mile south of the graveyard there was recently found a "kitchen midden"; a huge heap of shells with the same amount of blown sand overlying it, and the same dark-stained streak in the sandbank.

Nowhere in the vicinity are there any traces of a camp, and from this it can be readily inferred that it was previous to the coming of the hated Roman that a preference was given to this locality.

Another waggish suggestion is, that the savage hillmen spent their summer holidays, considerably over two thousand years ago, in Amble, then a seaside resort—a privilege now claimed by the sister hamlet.

THE ROMAN PERIOD

Of the Roman invasion and occupation of Britain there is very little trace in or around Amble, with the exception of a fragment of an altar stone found near Gloster Hill. It is evident there must have been a small camp here, but no trace can be found. About two miles in a straight line west is Chester House, and, further on, near Swarland is Chester Hill, which seems a sort of connecting link, certainly of a strong Roman flavour. In all probability there is a road connecting these stations with the " Devil's Causeway " which passes north near Framlington; but no real trace has yet been found. Although mention is made in old documents of local names it will be readily admitted that there was very little opposition on the low-lying lands; it was only in the fastness of his native hills that the ancient Celt felt his strength, and offered a stubborn resistance to the all-powerful militant invader.   Hence we might assume that with no serious opposition the Roman occupation of the district was of a temporary and a peaceful nature.

SAXON TIMES

The Saxon invasion and ultimate supremacy over the natives has left no trace here, nor is there any historical trace of the ruthless Dane who murdered and pillaged whole tracts of Northumberland near the coast.

There is a story to which some credence is given, but which is eschewed by the historian, viz. that a fleet of Vikings during the early invasion of Britain anchored in the river at a point where it was exceptionally wide, scoured out by the effect of the circuitous course of the river to the mouth; and some people assert that fragments of this type of ship have been found in the deep alluvial deposits near the old river-bed.

The Jutes, Angles, and Saxons, invaded Britain by running their flat-bottomed, high-prowed boats into the rivers all along the coast, and from the numerous villages of un-doubted Saxon origin on the Coquet from the

sea to the Cheviots. It is every way likely
that the mouth of the Coquet was used as a
landing-place; besides, there is historical
proof that they founded Warkworth where
there still exists a good many traces of the
primitive Anglo-Saxon village. There is,
however, no trace of the old-time village in
Amble so graphically described by Grant
Allen in Anglo-Saxon Britain, which is well
worth giving here.

"Each little village of the English community possessed a general independence of
its own, and lay apart from all the others,
often surrounded by a broad belt, or mark of
virgin forest. It consisted of a clearing, like
those of the American backwoods, where a
single family or kindred had made its home
and preserved its separate independence
intact. In the middle of the clearing, surrounded by a wooden stockade, stood the
village; a group of rude, detached huts. The
marksmen each possessed a separate little
homestead, consisting, usually, of a small
wooden house or shanty, a courtyard, and a
cattle-fold. But while, in America, the clearing is only a temporary phase, and the border
of forest is soon cut down so as to connect

the village with its neighbours, in the old
Saxon fatherland the border of woodland
heath, or fen was jealously guarded as a
frontier and natural defence for the little pre-
datory and agricultural community. Whoever
crossed it was bound to give notice of his
coming by blowing a horn, else he was cut
down immediately as a stealthy enemy. The
marksmen wished to remain separate from all
others, and only to mix with those of their
own kin. In this primitive love of separation
we have the germ of that local independence,
and that isolated homelife which is one of the
most marked characteristics of the modern
Englishman."

Judging from this description it is just
possible that where Amble now stands was
the boundary of the clearing for the village
of Warkworth, where the stranger was under
the obligation of giving a signal of his
approach with a winding horn. Probably, too,
the south bank of the Coquet was the outside
radius, hence the lack of Anglo-Saxon traces
in Amble.

One history of Northumberland states that
foundations of Saxon buildings have been
found, but the authority for such a statement

must have been very slender, as not a fragment of proof is in existence; in spite of the fact that numerous excavations have been made during the past half-century.

Of course there was a monastery on Coquet Isle in Saxon times, for we are told in the life of Saint Cuthbert that he visited the monastery to lend his aid in council on matters pertaining to the spread of Christianity amongst the rude barbarous Saxons of the North-Humber-Land. In all probability Amble, if there was an Amble, would have some connection with the monastery, but records of these far-off dark days are exceptionally rare.

THE COMING OF THE
CONQUEROR

The advent of the Normans changed the old order of things in England, and from that date Amble finds a place in history. After the division of the spoils we find the manors of Ambell were amongst other grants of land given to the Tynemouth Priory by the powerful noble Robert de Mowbray in 1090.

By some peculiar freak of fortune Amble was not destined to be a militant village with all the pomp and pageantry of the period, when the clang of arms rang out from early morn to dewy eve, and for almost five centuries the peaceful husbandman's only conquest was the stubborn clay deposited by the great ice floe of the glacial age.

In all the priory-held land scattered over the district demesne, lands to the extent of forty-four and a half acres in the South Flat; thirty acres in the East Flat; fifteen acres in the West Flat; seven acres in the Crooks; twenty-three acres in Dolake Law; two and a

25

half roods in Syket Meadow at the north side of the Hope; three roods in the Syket Meadow under Gonuldes Cross; six acres in the West Meed at Blakelaw; one and a quarter acres in the West Meed, and twenty acres in the Strothers.

After many inquiries I have failed to find any connection with the names of fields, etc., coming down to the present day.

There were eighteen tenants who asserted they were freeholders, and twenty-two bond-holders who amongst them held four hundred and sixty-three acres. Besides land the priory held many other privileges, such as salt pans, coal mines, coney warrens, fishing rights, etc.

Terms were made with the Baron of Warkworth to grind the tenants corn for a certain moulture (one fourteenth), and the demesne lands corn to be ground free. A rent charge of 40s. to be paid to the priory out of the mill. Also timber for three ploughs, and so many loads of timber from my lord's wood at Warkworth. In 1328, the twenty-two tenants paid as "housmale" 7s. 4d. a year in money and rendered in labour, eggs, and fowls, £5, 12s. 8d.; of which 20s. was expended in charges.

A pasture called Vilkemes yielded a rent of

5s., and certain meadows were let for 40s.—
de fortissimo diversis tenentibus—41s.; 7s.
2d. was paid for Abbotsooth; fifteen cottages
paid 12s. 9d.; 40s. was received from Warkworth Mill; but the Scodewell fishing was
unlet, and the cane fishing and the marsh lands
provided nothing. In the following year the
fishing was let to one Batey of Amble for £5.

About this time Richard de Twing, Prior of
Tynemouth (1320-1339), granted short leases
of parcels of demesne land. Roger, son of
William of Hauxley, obtained four acres near
Blakelaw for eight years at 8d. per acre.
John, son of Thomas of Amble, two acres,
William Pickenett, four acres, John Allison
of Hauxley, four acres lying near Gonuldees
Cross, for similar periods at similar rentals.
According to these records land in Amble in
those days was to be had at a cheap rate com-
pared with the present day, and a noticeable
instance is that a small allotment of five
acres is now let at an annual rent equal to the
total rental value of the whole township, but
of course there is a considerable difference in
money value.

At various periods the monks were called
upon to prove their claims to the Manor of
Ambell and Hauxley, which they seem to have

sustained.   It is generally admitted that the monks were indulgent landlords, and down till the dissolution of the monasteries in 1536 life in Amble seems to have been of the ding-dong order.

The dissolution, with its consequent devastation of the monasteries, brought the land in Amble to be the property of the King, who laid claim to the money, goods, and chattels of the wealthy priory.   The Crown seems to have been a much more exacting landlord than the monks, for in 1580, the tenants were reported to be ready to give up their holdings.   At the dissolution there were fourteen tenants and seven cottages in Amble.   In the Ministers account 1539, John Widdrington, bailiff, accounts for £15, 12s. 6d., being rents received from twenty-one copyholders, for their holdings.   For pasture called Wild Mere mede £5, 2s. 6d., the value of twenty-four quarters of barley paid in kind by the fourteen tenants, one quarter six bushels a piece;   £1, 6s. 8d. for fourscore salt fish accruing from four cobbles; one shilling for a cottage; six shillings for the fines of assize of bread and ale, according to the ancient custom, and for the pannage of swine, a total of £22, 14s. 6d.   Eventually the Crown

QUEEN STREET, AMBLE.

[*Photo by J. Thistle.*]

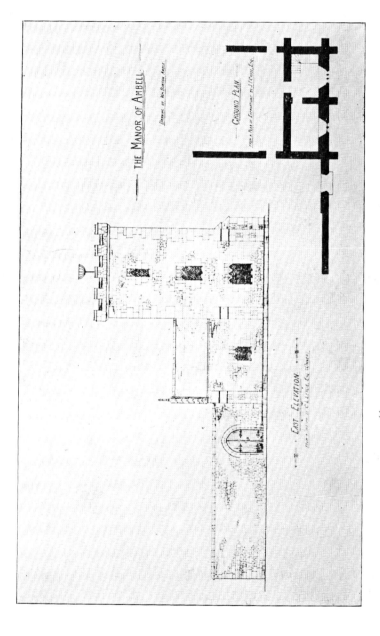

THE MANOR OF AMBELL

GROUND PLAN

EAST ELEVATION

"YE ANCIENTE MANOR HOUSE."

lands were sold by Charles II. in 1628 to the London Corporation, who resold it to various gentlemen of London and the Provinces.

During the possession of Amble by the Crown, almost a hundred years, the Manor of Amble increased in value the small sum of £2, 8s. The grant to the London Corporation included " The township of Ambell with lands in the tenure of diverse persons at the lord's will, of the yearly value of £15, 13s. 6d., twenty-four quarters and four bushels of barley annually by the fourteen tenants, that is to say, one quarter and six bushels by each tenant valued at £6, 2s. 6d. per annum; a cottage worth twelve pence yearly; all the rents of assize of bread and ale payable by the tenants there, amounting to six shillings yearly; the pannage of swine payable by fourteen tenants there, viz. by every tenant one penny. All that Manor House on site in the street of Ambell than or late in the tenure of Robert Bullock worth 3s. 4d. per annum; the site of a salt pit or salt pan worth 4s. per annum; the coal mines there valued at 41s. per annum; a coneygarth worth 10s. per annum the whole amount worth £25, 2s. 6d."

In all acounts there is the assize of bread and ale, and is explained thus: " All the tennents there have ancientlie paid for the assize of bread and ale, 6s. per annum, by custom only, by which they give licence to someone to brew and bake within the Manor, and at present they have licensed one Elizabeth Gibson, who payeth yearly 6s."

Is this the origin of the licensed victualler? If so, on this score at least, we cannot congratulate the present age on its progress in the control of licences, as the few people of Amble in 1608 had absolute control of the licence as well as local option.

At a later date the bulk of the land in Amble with the many manorial privileges were conveyed to Sir William Fenwick of Meldon. Adhering to the King in the Civil War of the Commonwealth, his estates were confiscated, but by some peculiar means, not quite clear, the Amble estates passed to his daughter, who married Sir Francis Radcliffe, afterwards first Earl of Derwentwater, by whose descendants the estates were held down to the memorable rising in the Stuart cause in 1715. James, the third Earl of Derwentwater and his brother, Charles Radcliffe, espoused the cause of the Stuarts, for which they both paid the penalty with their lives, besides the confiscation of all their property and land to the Crown. Charles Radcliffe, having previously married Charlotte, Countess of Newborough, provisions were made for their descendants. Afterwards by an Act of Parliament in the reign of George III., 1798, all the Manor of Amble, the farms, lands, hereditaments and premises, with their royalties, members, and appurtenances in Amble, Hauxley and Warkworth, as the said William Radcliffe held, the same at the time of his death were granted by letters patent, to Anthony James, Earl of Newborough and his heirs.

These estates, comprising the Manor or Lordship of Amble, thereby two old bolls and four bushels of barley payable each year at the Candlemas by the tenants of Amble; a free warren or .coneygarth at Amble and Hauxley; a smith's shop at Amble; the coal mines at Amble and Hauxley; salt pans at Amble; five farms of land called Hope House; and two farms of land at Hauxley called the Hauxley Fields; a burgess' house, garth, and four stints in Warkworth; three farms and a coney waren at Togston Moor Houses, commonly called the Low Hall, of the total value of £262, 12s.

At the death of the Countess of Newborough in 1853, the estates passed to her husband, Lieutenant Colonel Charles Leslie, and to his heirs.   These estates have recently been sold, the major portion being secured by Sir Christopher Furness, which severs another link with the past history of Amble.

In 1663, the following also held parcels of land in Amble, viz. Nicholas Lewing, Robert Widdrington, Edward Cook, William Smith, Edward Browell, John Taylor, and William Reid.   From the aforementioned freeholders and Sir Francis Radcliffe, the title deeds of all the land in Amble hold their origin.   The following interesting notes are taken from the new "County History," Warkworth section.

"On the 24th of April, 1656, William Smith of Togston, William Reid of Amble, and G. Bullock of Amble entered into agreement with Edward Browell and John Taylor, whereby it was agreed to divide their lands lying in Amble East Field which lay mixed together and very inconvenient by reason whereof many strifes and differences do ofttimes arise."

Smith and Reid were to have two farms near the sea, Browell and Taylor were to have two farms lying next to long dyke, and Bullock's half farm was to be in the middle. The old grey slated cottage at the west end of the town, adjoining what is known as the Green Field, was the farm-house of the Bullocks and was not sold with the land, which passed by purchase to Smith and Taylor who divided the estate between them in 1745.

Another paragraph says:

" On the 31st July, 1660, Robert Widdrington, Nicholas Lewing, John Taylor, Edward Browell, and William Reid, styled the neighbours of Amble, entered into an agreement with Edward Cook, whereby the latter agreed to allow, during pleasure, a free way out of the west end of Amble, and from this yeat then to a place called the west yeat, and from the said west yeat straight up a rig thereon; using two rigs at most; straight up to the Rye Haven way, and then keeping that way for all occasions of the said neighbours, and that all the said neighbours should have liberty from 14th day of June to the 1st day of July yearly, and no longer, to lead whins from the Sloe Wicket."

There are good reasons to believe that the way out of Amble referred to is what is now known as the Acklington Road. One reason for this is that the March Dyke is on the south side of the road, thereby causing the Gloster Hill Farm, which originally belonged to the New Hall (the donor of the right of way), to be saddled with the upkeep of the fence on both sides of the highway.

Of the seven freeholders previously mentioned, the lands in the Smith family are the only estates held in the old name. The Lewings' lands were bought up by the Radcliffes, the Reid and Browell's farms passed by purchase and succession to Taylor, and thence to Wellwood, and ultimately to Alexander Wellwood Ratteray (through his wife), who sold the estates, the greater portion of which were secured by the Lawson-Smith trustees in 1875.

The Widdrington estates passed by purchase, by an order of the Court of Chancery, to Edward Werge of Horton of Glendale, in 1807, who afterwards sold a portion of the estate in small parcels. The main portion of the estate now known as Amble Moor House was purchased by Mr James Dand, of Chevington Wood Side, by whom it was passed on and is now in the possession of Mr J. T. Dand.

The detached portion of the Widdrington

estate extended from the river on the north, on each side of the Wynd in a straight line to Mark's Row, a large portion of which was bought by Richardson and Douglas in 1810, and is now in the possession of Messrs Rutherford, Richardson, Duncan, Brown, Ward, Mason, etc.

The different portions of the Taylor-Wellwood estates, not included in the purchase by the Lawson-Smith trustees in 1875, comprised chiefly the licensed premises and land adjoining what is known as the Wellwood Arms in High Street; this was purchased by James Lamb, Brewer, Warkworth, and is still in the possession of that family.

Amble House with outbuildings, gardens, and land adjoining was purchased by the late Dr Currie, which passed, on his death, to his wife, now Mrs Dr Smyth. The site, known as No. 1 on the bill of sale, next to Amble House, extends from High Street to Bede Street, now forming the west side of Wellwood Street, was bought by Messrs R. Carse & Son. The site of Bede Street, Edwin Street, etc., was purchased by Mr Potts, but was afterwards resold to Messrs R. Carse & Son.

A HUNDRED YEARS AGO AND NOW

At the beginning of the nineteenth century, Amble was divided into three farms. Hedley's Farm at the west end. The farmyard was situated on the site, and near what is now Gibson Street; part of the buildings being incorporated in the present houses. The three low, one-storied cottages opposite, were the housing accommodation—the two-roomed one acting as the farm-house.

Close by stood the farm-house of the Link Farm, and the farm steading was on the site of the now blacksmith's shop in Albert Street. The other was the Link House Farm, the Wellwood Arms public-house being the farm-house with the farm steading adjoining.

The principal occupation of the few cottagers in the winter-time of these days was the use of the thrail, and the thrail man thrashed the corn on the earthen floor of his living-room. There was also a tithe barn where

we now have Walker's Yard. Close by is
another bit of old Amble with the date 1749,
and the inscription R $\overset{\text{H}}{}$ M on the massive
$\underset{1749}{}$
door-head. This house belonged to a family
named Hudson, the last of whom was an old
lady named Tibby Hudson, who sold the cottage and adjoining land to John Turner, and
eventually ended her days in an alms-house.
At the corner of Wellwood Street in line with
Amble House and Wellwood Arms there were
four one-story cottages two of which are still
standing. Another low, thatched cottage
stood in High Street, which, together with
Amble House, the residence of Squire Taylor,
and those already mentioned, comprised the
sum-total of Amble one hundred years ago .

Previous to the building of the harbour,
Amble did not extend beyond what is now
known as Wellwood Street. The harbour
contractor during a delay in the contract,
with a keen eye to business, built a large
block of property at the top end of Queen
Street, extending into Church Street, long
known as Welch's Buildings, which also included a public-house. Captain Parry, an old
soldier who had served at Waterloo, rented

the public-house for his son, and named it after the famous battle.

A little later another contractor named Sanderson, who built the railway bridge near Morwick, constructed a large block of buildings on the opposite side of the street, extending to Cross Street, which also included a public-house, the Dock Hotel.

This block was known as Sanderson's Buildings. Eventually more buildings followed, forming the principal street—which ultimately became Queen Street.

From this time Amble ceased to be an agricultural village, and agriculture was forced to give way to the slow but steady march of the mining industry. The west end portion of Queen Street dates from 1840; the lower portion extending to Bridge Street developed with the extension of Broomhill Colliery in the later 'seventies. About this time Mr Hugh Andrews took over the management of Broomhill Colliery, and with marvellous business tact and ability the output in a short time was more than doubled, and Broomhill coals were in demand in almost every port in Europe. The harbour was acquired from Messrs Harrison & Co., lessees of Radcliffe Colliery, and extensions and alterations were undertaken to improve the entrance. A large fleet of sailing ships owned by the same enterprising gentleman conveyed the coal chiefly to foreign ports, and it is needless to add that the mushroom growth of Amble from this time was entirely due to the rare business capacity of Mr Hugh Andrews.

Church Street comprises what was originally known as " the Sea Lonnen." This old road to the seashore was the boundary between Smith and Taylor's lands, from the top of Church Street to the site of the present vicarage. A little farther on by the side of the same highway Mr T. G. Smith built a school-house in 1855, and gave it over to a committee of management appointed by the inhabitants, and it was long known in local parlance as the " Lonnen School." In 1903, a trust deed was granted to a body of trustees by Mr E. M. Lawson Smith, heir to the Smith estates in Amble. With the advent of free education it was conveyed to the County Council Education Committee who have again, on the completion of the new Council Schools, resold it to the Urban authority.

" Blue Bell Lane," now Albert Street is part of old Amble together with Marks Row, a long street of low, one-story cottages with a small portion of old-time cobble stone street, situated on the road to Radcliffe.

The rest of Amble is comparatively modern, comprising the extensive building development on the late Mr Carse's land at the west end; the several new streets extending from Church Street to the railway, and the numerous new streets at the harbour. These extensions constitute the extraordinary development which transformed a tiny agricultural village into a prosperous, modern, industrial town in the space of a century.

EARLY TRADING

From the very early times, at least from the Saxon invasion of Britain, ships have entered the River Coquet by the entrance which is now known as the "old water," anchored in the river, and paid toll at the old Manor House. The trade in those far-off days was doubtless small, but the commencement of the foundry at Acklington Park in 1775, gave an impetus to Amble as a trading port. Before the days of the steam engine, water was the great motive-power, and advantage was taken of the River Coquet at this point for commercial purposes.

A company was formed and an enormous dam constructed from the plans of the famous engineer, Robert Smeaton of Eddystone fame, at considerable expense. Extensive rolling mills, with all the necessary machinery, were erected, and the crude tin ore was conveyed in small ships to Amble, or rather to a place on the River Coquet near Amble.

This comprised a harbour and quay all combined on the river-bank at a place known in later days as the " granary."

At this time the road to Warkworth was by way of Gloster Hill and Gildean. The foundry company, however, made a road to their landing-stage storehouse, and this was the beginning of the present road to Warkworth, and the old storehouse, while it remained, was a well-known landmark.

The crude ore was carted to the foundry by way of Gloster Hill and Acklington, and the manufactured article was recarted back and taken away in ships to industrial centres. This very enterprising company was, however, short-lived, and, as a matter of course, Amble as a trading port ceased to be of any great importance down to the construction of the harbour in 1836, some sixty-one years later.

The road from the foundry's storehouse to Warkworth by the Beal Bank was completed later; and " alang the Warkworth road past the ' granary ' " (which was situated about midway between Warkworth and Amble) was a very familiar phrase in Amble until it was pulled down some years ago to build a pretty cottage at the top of the Beal Bank. The name " granary " is, in all probability, derived from the storage of grain in the building (after the collapse of the foundry), awaiting the arrival of small craft, delayed on their passage to the miniature port on the Coquet, prior to the introduction of railways. In later years it was converted into fishermen's dwellings of a very crude type, and, eventually, becoming a timber warehouse, for which it was used until it became too ruinous to be of any use whatever.

EARLY INDUSTRIES

From very remote days Amble has had an industrial turn, for we read that the Baron of Warkworth, in 1178, gave a grant to the monks of Newminster Abbey to make salt in the Gildean Burn. The site of this old-time industry was near Gloster Hill, traces of which were found a few years ago. It seems from this time onward salt making was a regular industry in Amble, as there are very frequent references to salt pans in old documentary notices. At a recent date salt pans occupied a site near Victoria Street, at the foot of the Wynd, also near the site of the present harbour; and at a comparative recent date salt was made on the Links—the buildings used for the manufacturing purposes still remaining. In the making of salt, apart from the primitive method of natural evaporation, a good deal of fuel is required, and as wood became scarce it became necessary to use coal.

44

In 1538, Leyland states, writing of Coquet Island, "that there was abundance of sea coal, which men dig in the clives or cliffs, which they find very good." Passing along the shore from Amble Harbour to Hauxley an extraordinary number of pit shafts are to be seen. These occur in great profusion opposite the island, which goes to prove that the island mining was extended to the mainland. In 1611 a Royal Commission appointed for the survey of mines in the Counties of Durham and Northumberland gives a peculiar and interesting report of these mining operations.

" By examination of the tennents of Auxley it is affirmed that the mynes of cole are drowned yet there is myne of cole enough if the water could be overcomed. The Pitts are eight or nine fathoms in deepenness and threequarters in thickenness; a reasonable good burning cole but what charge will wynn the said myne cannot certainly be knowen neither what seem of cole can or maybe discovered.

" Thomas Tweedy of Ambell aged fortie years, one of the Hewers within the said cole pit, there by space of seven years sayeth that there is only one pit wrought, and now in the tenure of Edmund Fynch and Henry Kirton by lease or covenant from one Mr Hummerstone. He sayeth that pitts are in deepenness 4, 5, and 6 fathoms and the seame half a yard thick, a caking cole fit for fire or salt pans. There is great quantities of myne to endure for many years if the water could be drawn or wonn, the roof is bad and falls of itself. He sayeth they could work more if there were more vent or sale, and is verille persuaded that his master doe not gyne above £10 per annum, and knoweth of noe other myne there likely to be discovered."

This rather peculiar mining seems to have been principally for salt making, and at this early age there seems also to have been a strong tendency in Amble towards a budding mining centre, rather than a rural village.

From what we can gather, however, the art of mining was of the most primitive order. No timber was used, only a small burrow was made near the shaft, while all the coal was not removed from the roof in order not to loosen the stone above. Ventilation and light was entirely of the natural order; the light of day, the necessary illuminant, and the air in the shaft was sufficient for ventilation, hence the extraordinary number of shafts which, according to an old plan, numbered eighty, extending from Amble to Hauxley. The water seems to have been the greatest source of trouble, especially when it could not be drained by a drift to the dip of the seam. As time wore on these difficulties, as well as many others, were overcome by the march of scientific education and commercial enterprise.

In 1826, an enterprising gentleman commenced mining operations in the millfield near Hauxley on a more extensive scale than heretofore. With the present-day advantage of the science of geology we don't wonder that this venture for extensive mining was abortive. It was, however, the means of a further experiment, the success of which heralded the dawn of the industrial progress of Amble and district.

Ten years later sinking operations commenced near by, afterwards named Radcliffe Colliery in honour of the Royalty owners who were descended from the old family of Radcliffe. It is generally supposed that the original Harbour Company commenced the operations at Radcliffe, but in reality it was a gentleman from Bedlington who had pre-viously speculated in the Sleekburn Colliery.

Having come to the conclusion that the new venture was a bad speculation after being won, he sold it to the new Harbour Company which had recently been formed.

THE HARBOUR

There can be little doubt that it was the sinking operations at Radcliffe that gave the making of a harbour at Amble a practical turn. It is said that the idea first occurred to a local solicitor who migrated to London. Being actuated by the successful sinking operations at Radcliffe he induced a few wealthy friends to form a company to build a harbour at Amble. Consequently, in 1837, the Harbour Company was formed, and a parliamentary grant was obtained the same year, and from this, dates the real progress of Amble as an industrial centre.

The first Commissioners included the Earl of Newborough and the trustees of his estate (owners of the Royalty); the lessees of Radcliffe Colliery who had the right to have two representatives on the Board of Commissioners, besides thirteen other gentlemen, three of whom were to be appointed by the Duke of Northumberland.

Five years were allowed to complete the harbour, but by an Act of Parliament, passed five years later, the time was extended for an additional five years, and no toll was to be demanded until £10,000 had been expended. The Duke of Northumberland, having successfully contended that the salmon fishing would be damaged by the making of a harbour, claimed and was awarded £10,000.

Out of the four plans submitted by competition to the famous engineer, Sir John Rennie, the one which culminated in the present harbour was adopted. Eventually the contract was let and the erstwhile obscure tiny village was suddenly invaded by crowds of workmen.

The contractor at an early stage of the proceedings built a rather pretentious domicile on the edge of the high cliff—a point of vantage which overlooked the whole scene of operations. Besides doing duty as a residence it was also the " Tommy Shop " where the workmen on the job procured their stores in lieu of wages prior to the passing of the " Truck Act." A large room in the building was also set apart for religious worship, and a Catholic priest from Longhorsely ministered to the spiritual needs of his co-religionists.

The stones for building the south pier were procured from the Pan Haven Rocks, and afterwards from the quarry near the cliff. From the rocks a gangway was constructed and a small puffing billy, one of the first of its kind, conveyed the stones to the pier The material for the north pier was taken over the river by a bridge constructed for the purpose a little above the site of the present brick-works. The piers were constructed eighty-three yards apart, and a quay wall was built for trading purposes on the south side of the harbour, principally for the shipment of coal. It soon became apparent that the stones used for the construction of the piers were ill-suited for such use ; and a few years hence the work had to be done over again—using granite from Scotland.

The north pier, owing to the force of the north-east storms, has always been a source of continual anxiety to the Commissioners down to the present day. With the great development of the local collieries, and the corresponding increase in the volume of trade, in 1890, it was decided to improve the entrance to the harbour by extending the north pier. In this the contractor failed, and the work was carried out by the

Commissioner's own men. Quite recently there has been a considerable extension of the south pier carried out, which has resulted in acting as a screen for the sand, which previously used to accumulate on the bar. Still another advantage accrues from this extension scheme, viz. that the storms now deposit sand inside the harbour where the dredger can work it out, and has, consequently, resulted in allowing ships of large tonnage to enter the port.

In order to facilitate this later work a jetty was constructed joining up the quay proper with the old south pier, and this has added a twofold object of utility and pleasure. In the first place, the material used for the construction was prepared and taken by this easy means to the work on the pier, and, secondly, a delightful promenade was provided. A complete circuit can now be made besides providing easy access to the charming, all-round view from the cliff. It is unnecessary to add that this promenade is now the most attractive part of Amble at all seasons of the year. In the summer months it is especially enjoyable, as from here there is an uninterrupted view of the gorgeous northern sunset, and the clear, pure air bristling with a touch of the Polar regions, together with

the mighty storms which dash against the
north pier the consequent mountains of spray,
to not a few are a no less genuine pleasure.
Altogether the harbour has cost about a
quarter of a million, and the bondholders at
the present time are the Broomhill Collieries
Company Limited.

THE NEW AMBLE

At the completion of the harbour in 1844, Amble appeared in a new aspect, and claimed to rank as a small seaport in spite of the fact that the name Warkworth Harbour was given to the new undertaking.

The following crude lines, after allowing for bad rhyme, bad grammar, etc., we must admit that in the main the prophetic vein is excellent, and a good deal more than the poet of sixty years ago prophesied has become a reality in Amble.

ON AMBLE

" Near the mouth of the Coquet, that bonny clear river,
   Stands Amble now famed for commerce and trade,
But a very few years since, no one believed ever
   So flourishing now it could have been made.

The town's much enlarged, the shops with gas lighted,
   A taste for improvement pervades through the same;
Only look at the buildings, you'll then be delighted
   To see how fair Amble is rising in fame.

When the branch line of railway once is completed,
  Amble's importance will rise in the scale;
The plans of its friends will not be defeated,
  Such praiseworthy schemes ought never to fail.

The inns are commodious, the landladies cheerful,
  Where strangers and guests may have a good cheer,
For where could be found a much better place full
  O' gin, rum, and brandy, and plenty strong beer.

There are bakers and grocers, drapers and tailors,
  Keelmen and trimmers, if I knew when to stop,
And the town's often crowded with fine jolly sailors,
  Some wending their way to yon neat barber's shop.

There's a postman from Alnwick comes twice every
      day,
  The great herald of strange news from afar,
Also three worthy teachers that point out the way
  To know the laws of yon bright shining star.

When sick or unwell there are doctors abounding,
  Whence a dose of strong physic will make well
      again,
Or a lump of good chalk, if the name's not
    astounding,
  Will free all at once from a rheumatic pain.

The prospects from Amble are highly commanding,
  The wide German Ocean spread out to the view,
Whence the bold sons of Neptune with canvas
    expanding,
  Sail into the harbour a fine jovial crew.

The harbour has water for ships of great burden
  To enter and sail up with ease to the quay,
To heave out the ballast or take in a lading
  O' coals from yon canny coal pit, you'll agree.

Then success to the harbour and Radcliffe coal pit,
  And may the prospects of Amble still flourish,
And we'll pledge in a bumper just here where we sit,
  That these feelings for aye we will cherish."

The first Gas Company was formed in 1848, and a rather humorous story is told of the opposition to the new light.   At this time there was a small tallow candle factory in Amble (now a lost industry), principally for local use, and the candle manufacturer swore that he would give a shock to the new Gas Company.

In due course he started for Russia, to bring home some tallow the like of which had never been seen in Amble, and which would produce a light that would put the gas in the shade.   Fortunately for the Gas Company the enterprising candle maker never returned from his long journey, and what became of him is a mystery to this day.

In those days the postman came from Alnwick, and from the ducal town all affairs were managed by the Alnwick Rural Sanitary Authority.   By a gradual growth of population in 1869 it became necessary to provide a burial-ground, for which on all previous occasions the mother parish had found a churchyard. After the Order of Council this year, forming the ecclesiastical Parish of Amble, powers were given to levy a rate on the new district for burial purposes. In due course a joint Burial Board was appointed for the townships of Amble, Togston, Hauxley and Gloster Hill.

The site ultimately selected for the new cemetery was a portion of the Links near the Link House Farm, comprising two and a half acres. At the entrance there is an imposing building divided into two chapels, for the Church of England and the Dissenters respectively, and in the south-west corner there is a superintendent's house of a similar style of architecture. One half of the new God's acre was set apart for the members of the Established Church and the other half for the Nonconformists, which also included a small plot set apart for the use of the Roman Catholic body.

Twenty-five years later the Parish Councils Act slightly changed the constitution and name of the Burial Board, which became a joint Burial Committee of fifteen, made up *pro rata* from the different townships. Amble, nine. Gloster Hill, one. Hauxley, three, and Togston Terrace, two.

Soon after the change it became apparent that the original cemetery was too limited, and negotiations were opened to have it extended near the same site.

During the negotiations it transpired that, owing to the great erosion of the sea-banks close by, it would necessitate the new portion to be in a more inland position.

Eventually eleven acres were purchased at the extreme west end of the town. Less than one-half of this has been recently laid out in a truly artistic fashion. Unlike the previous sandy waste the present cemetery is surrounded by a belt of trees and shrubs, forming a sort of halo round the new God's acre where the rude fathers of this and later generations will cease from troubling, and sleep in peace.

THE LOCAL BOARD

As the population of Amble kept on increasing, and, having secured the powers of a Burial Board, the management of local affairs by the Alnwick Authority became very irksome. The carrying-out of a sewerage scheme in 1875, which cost the enormous sum of £2200, and the series of blunders connected with the undertaking, naturally caused a great deal of ill-feeling against this body.

Accordingly, an application was made to the Local Government Board for Amble to be made a Local Board District, which was granted after the necessary inquiry. A local humorist depicted the Election in a comic picture—the candidates climbing a greasy pole. The likeness to the different celebrities, the characteristic attitudes of the candidates, the witticisms emanating from the crowd, stamps it not only a humorous but a remarkably clever cartoon.

The property qualification, one of the great anomalies of the past, held good, and no one but the property man was considered sufficiently intellectual to take part in the newly formed Local Board. The new Board consisted of nine members, and the successful candidates out of the twenty-four nominations were as follows in the voting order. Messrs M. H. Dand, Dr Currie, H. Andrews, Thos. Leighton, M. Douglas, John Douglas, Thos. Campbell, R. G. McInnes and Edward Spence. Mr Dand was appointed Chairman, Dr Currie, Medical Officer, Mr Gibson, Clerk, and Mr G. Beattie was appointed Surveyor and Inspector of Nuisances.

Naturally enough there was a spirit of drastic economy in the newly appointed body which resulted in the barely necessary sanitary reforms, the chief aim and object of the early city fathers was to keep down the rates. In later years this penny-wise economy was obvious, as will be seen in the recent street improvements, new sewers, etc.; in fact the whole town has had to be remodelled at a very great cost to later-day ratepayers. For some considerable time there was no report of the proceedings, afterwards there was a

HIGH STREET, AMBLE.

[*Photo by W. G. Chambers.*

BEDE STREET, AMBLE.

[*Photo by W. G. Chambers.*]

ORIGINAL HARBOUR ENTRANCE.

[*Photo by G. Waters.*

THE HARBOUR, AMBLE.

[*Photo by A. Adamson.*

brief report sent by the clerk to the Alnwick papers. Later, the Press applied and were permitted to attend the meetings, and the doings of the Amble Local Board reported, if not very edifying for an august body, were to say the least always humorous reading. As the population increased the water supply from the various wells and pumps gave out, and the local authorities were confronted with the task of having to provide a new water supply. While Amble remained a village the old wells provided a plentiful supply of water from the quicksand bed underlying the boulder clay outcropping in the banks of the old river-bed. Besides, this source could be struck all over the vicinity at a depth varying from ten to twenty feet of boulder clay and sand.

At the harbour a seam of coal, previously worked at the depth of a few fathoms, provided an ample supply for a time. In fact, previous to the Hauxley and Togston Water Supply, the inhabitants of Radcliffe Colliery were supplied from the harbour pump in the summer months, the water being carted to the colliery village and retailed at $\frac{1}{2}$d. per can.

Naturally with the great growth of the town there existed a doubt that sewerage was percolating into the source of the natural springs, and, eventually, the Hall Bank well, an ample supply for the ancient husbandmen, was considered inadequate for the needs of a modern industrial town.

After a long search the surveyor, Mr William Gibson, located a water-shed near Hazon, six miles distant, and preparations were being made to carry out a big water scheme for Amble. But the Fates decided that the days of Local Board rule were coming to an end, and the Parish Councils Act of 1894, did away with the old authority, after being in existence for nineteen years.

URBAN DISTRICT COUNCIL

By the Parish Councils Act Amble became an Urban area, and the new authority, i.e. the Urban District Council had slightly extended powers.

The property qualification was taken away, and the greatest anomaly of all, the proxy property vote was abolished. These restrictions removed, twenty-seven candidates entered the lists, and considerable interest was taken in the more modern form of election. The successful candidates were as follows: Messrs James Earnshaw, Joseph Bowran, Robert G. McInnes, John T. Carse, Thomas Douglas, George Burton, Joseph R. Tuck, Thomas Matthews, and Thomas L. McAndrews.

One of the provisions of the new Act was that the Chairman of Urban District Councils would be, ex officio, Justice of the Peace for the county during the term of his office; and the honour fell to Mr James Earnshaw.

The Hazon Water Scheme had previously been adopted by the Local Board, but to this scheme a section of the new council was in strong opposition.

An alternate scheme was put forward, viz. to pump a supply from the River Coquet, which received a good deal of public support. Another scheme was also put forward in opposition to the Hazon Scheme, viz. to provide a supply from the Gloster Hill banks, the site of the present cemetery, but the shortage, and the fact that it was from the quicksand bed and liable to contamination from the farm steading and the sewerage, was fatal to this accredited cheap scheme from the first.

The chief objection to the Hazon Scheme was its supposed hardness, which ultimately proved to be twenty-one per cent, and the estimated cost £6600. For this sum was provided settle wells for the various springs (five in all) connected with a collecting reservoir, capable of holding 100,000 gallons; five miles of six-inch pipe to a service reservoir at Morwick, with a capacity of storing 1,000,000 gallons. The reservoir is about a mile distant from the town, on an elevated position one hundred and thirty-seven feet above sea-level. One acre of land was secured from the Duke of Northumberland at £150, which ultimately included the right to get a supply from the main at Acklington Factory and Morwick at 6d. per thousand gallons, besides the right to the overflow at the reservoir, if any. Added to this there was one mile of pipes to the town, the many ramifications of mains in the different streets, together with the various stand pipes, scour valves, fire hydrants, etc., necessary for an up-to-date water scheme.

In due course the L.G.B. inquiry was held, and although the opposition to the scheme was led by a solicitor, in the person of Mr Charles Percy of Alnwick, the Inspector refused to entertain either the opposition to the Hazon Scheme or the supposed advantages of the alternate schemes, and eventually the Hazon Water Scheme for Amble was approved by the L.G.B.

Mr M. Temple Wilson was appointed engineer, and the late Mr J. T. Carse, an enthusiastic supporter of the scheme, carried out the contract, and the much-opposed water scheme turned out to be an extraordinary boon to the people of Amble in many ways. Powers were granted by the L.G.B. to supply

E

the neighbouring townships of Togston Terrace and East Chevington, and the latter, which includes Broomhill Colliery, Red Row and Chevington Drift, are now supplied from the service reservoir at Morwick at 6d. per thousand gallons.

Owing to a stiff gradient in the trunk main track reducing the hydraulic main, the actual carrying capacity of the main was considerably limited for a time.

Quite recently, however, acting on the advice of the surveyor, Mr. W. Gibson, a loop line of pipes was constructed around the rising ground, and the main is now discharging one hundred and fifty gallons per minute into the service reservoir.

The original supply from the springs was estimated at one hundred and twenty gallons per minute, and during the past year this has been augmented by a bore hole at thirty-six fathoms tapping a further supply of seventy gallons per minute, making altogether one hundred and ninety gallons available, at all seasons.

The people of Amble are justly proud of their water supply which, for quantity, purity, and general excellence, will be hard to surpass, besides being a considerable source of revenue. One big mistake in the original scheme is admitted, viz. the L.G.B. pressed for greater storage and advocated a reservoir of much greater dimensions or a duplicate of the present one. The want of this is now felt in the annual cleansing, which causes considerable inconvenience to the people in the outlying districts at a higher level than Amble, the main draw from the by-pass.

In carrying out the water supply in the streets ample provision was made for coping with fires, and hydrants were put in at every sixty yards. A hose was provided to cover this distance, and a fire brigade appointed. With a head of eighty feet at the highest point it will be apparent that Amble is well provided in this respect. Bathrooms which, previous to the water supply, were solitary exceptions, are now the rule, and together with flush water-closets are a primary consideration in all new houses.

Although the water supply is undoubtedly the greatest success of the new regime Amble has, in a good many other ways, been re-modelled at a small cost to the ratepayers, and the Amble of to-day is generally admitted to be a thoroughly efficient town in every way with a remarkably low death rate.

THE OLD MANOR HOUSE

There is one solitary link which connects the present-day Amble with the past, viz. the scrap of ruin which represents a remnant of the old Manor House of the priory monks. From excavations carried out previous to the building of the Catholic school chapel in 1897, it seems to have been an extensive building at some period of its history. With the extensive manors of "Ambbell, Auxley, and Cocket Island" there would doubtless be enormous duties incurred in the business transactions which would be enacted at the Manor House.

The present ruin consists of a sixteenth-century window, and is "situate in the street of Ambell," on the brow of an eminence overlooking a terrace of the ancient bed of the River Coquet. Vessels entering the river in "Ye olden times" would in all probability anchor at this part of the river just under the Manor House. Besides many other privileges it is said that the monks had a right to levy toll on all vessels entering the river, but, judging from the then stilted condition of the river mouth, the numerous winding curves, the small population interested chiefly in agriculture, the revenue from trading vessels would be very small, as it would almost entirely be confined to the export of salt.

During the rule of the priory the old hall (a name by which it was known in later days) would be kept in good repair, but after the dissolution of the monasteries in 1536, the tenant of the Manor House often complained of its ruinous condition; and in the early part of the seventeenth century a complaint ran as follows—

"That the said Manor House is much ruined and ready to fall for want of repair; your petitioner hitherto having had noe allowance for repair, although he have been farmer for many years by past."

Eventually it fell into decay, but still remained very much in evidence, as the payment of the "Hall Corn" a peculiar old custom, was continued down to the early part of 1800.

This consisted of twenty-four quarters of barley, and was made by the tenants to the representative of the Lord of the Manor upon an appointed day, on the site and near the remains of the old Manor House, by being poured out upon a great white sheet and then measured up by the Lord's representative. The day appointed was the Feast of the Purification, or Candlemas Day the 2nd of February, and was kept as a general holiday throughout the district.

The popular sport of the time was cock fighting, and the public cock-pit is said to have stood on the site of Mr Edward Coulson's house near the Old Hall Bank Well. Thither they hied after being well regaled at the expense of "my Lord"; eventually ending the revels in the village inns, and stories have been handed down of right royal "sprees" at the payment of the Hall Corn.

Some historians assert that there was a monastic cell here, but a good deal of research work has failed to prove this, although probably a monk may have lived in some of the recesses of the buildings to minister to the spiritual wants of the lay brothers and others, who managed the monastery, tithes, and other affairs of the priory such as rents, Royalties, etc., together with the demesne lands which were extensive.

In recent years the site of the old manor has again reverted to the use of religion, and a Roman Catholic school chapel now stands on a portion of the foundations of the accredited monastic cell. An interesting description of the transition from the old to the new is given in an historical sketch of Catholic missions, and is worth recording.

"Well-nigh three hundred years passed away before the Catholic religion could again plant its foot in Amble, formerly so instinct with Catholic life. In the year 1840, the harbour works, then commencing, attracted a considerable number of Irish labourers, many of whom were lodged in wooden huts. The Rev. William Fletcher who was then stationed at Longhorsely, twelve miles distant, generously offered his services to provide for his poor fellow-Catholics. He continued, until his death from fever in the fatal year of 1847, to say Mass and preach on alternate Sundays, and occasionally on weekdays in the Hope Farm on the Links. After his death

the good work went on under his successor
the Rev. James Hubbesty who left Longhorsely in 1853, and is since dead, and the
Rev. John S. Rogerson, now the Right Rev.
Monseigneur Rogerson, D.D., English chaplain in Paris.   About this time, owing to the
cessation of the harbour works, the little
flock became reduced in numbers, and the
mission was served only once a month.   In
1859, the charge of the district was entrusted
to the Rev. Joseph Gibson, Alnwick, who
officiated occasionally until 1868.   From that
year Amble ceased to be one of the missions
of the diocese, and it was not until 1877, that
its name reappeared in the official list in the
Catholic Directory and Northern Calendar.
Steps were then taken, as the place was once
more growing in importance and population,
and a bequest had been made for the purpose
by the late Colonel Leslie, to re-establish the
mission on a more regular and durable foot-
ing; and the Rev. C. G. Smith of Felton
volunteered for the work.   With the hearty
co-operation of the Bishop the Right Rev.
Dr Chadwick, and the goodwill of Mr C. L.
Lisle of Hassop Hall, Derbyshire, in trust for
whom much of the land in Amble is held,
and the assistance of friends, he succeeded in

securing some parcels of land—on one of which stands the ruin of the Manor House of the monastery—and erecting a large and handsome school chapel. This was solemnly opened by the Bishop on the 22nd of June, 1879, the Feast of the Sacred Heart of Jesus as recounted in the chronicle of last year's calendar. Since that time the congregation has gradually increased, and the school has been opened with every prospect of success."

Thus the pious wishes of the late Countess of Newborough are at length in a large measure fulfilled. It is through her that the Leslie Trust estates at Amble are inherited. In her lifetime she contributed an annual sum for the service of the mission and ardently longed to see the day when it would be permanently established, but though she wellnigh attained the age of a hundred years that happiness was not vouchsafed her. Her successor, the late Colonel Leslie, cherished the same hope and desire, and left a legacy of £200 for the purpose, and the present owner has put on record his good intention as soon as the trust settlements will give him freedom of action.

The first resident priest was the Rev.

Edward Robert, a genial pastor now of Minsteracres, followed by the Rev. John Roth who eventually retired to a family rectory near the beautiful town of Emms on the Rhine.   For a short while the Rev. Canon Barnett now of Felton (Rev. J. Walmsley is now resident priest) ministered to the spiritual wants, and Amble was the Alma Mater of the Rev. Matthew Culley, now retired.   Next in order came the Rev. Matthew Foster now of Ellingham.   The Rev. Charles Dunn followed, and, after five years of strenuous work, owing to a wasting disease reluctantly retired from active duty and died the following year.   The Rev. M. Langshaw who succeeded died suddenly during the past year and the Rev. Michael Norris is now the resident priest.

CHURCH OF ENGLAND

Down to 1870 Warkworth Parish included Amble and attended to the spiritual wants of members of the Established Church in Amble. Owing doubtless to the great increase in the population an Order in Council in 1869 was issued, and the townships of Amble and Hauxley and Gloster Hill were detached from Warkworth and formed into a new Parish of Amble.

Accordingly a new church was built from the plans of Messrs Austin & Johnson, and opened for public worship in 1870.

The first incumbent was the Rev. A. O. Medd, who later removed to Bamborough, subsequently to Rothbury, where he died. He was followed by the Rev. James Fairbrother by whose untiring energy the Church of the Good Shepherd and the new schools at Radcliffe, besides the handsome Medd Memorial Schools were provided. Mr Fairbrother was afterwards removed to Warkworth. The Rev. Charles Baldwin was the next pastor, afterwards removed to Cramlington. Formerly the living was known as a rectory but this was found to be an error. It is now a vicarage, and the present vicar is the Rev. E. R. Dawe.*

CONGREGATIONAL CHURCH

With the exception of the Catholic Mission initiated by the Countess of Newborough previously alluded to, there had not existed any other place of public worship in Amble until 1848. In the march of this year a church was opened by a small body of Congregationalists. This building, situated near the top of the Wynd, was not of the orthodox ecclesiastical order but rather of the severe conventicle type of building.

The old chapel was superseded by a handsome new church in 1894, situated in a central position of the town. The following have from time to time served as ministers. The Revs. James Wood, Rogers, William Knox, William Stewart, William Nicholson, W. A. Kidd, Hopper, Joplin, Joseph Bowron,

* Rev. T. N. Dunscombe is now vicar.

Robert Teasdale, R. Jefferson, D. Foulis, and the present minister is the Rev. J. Wilkins.

THE WESLEYAN METHODISTS

In 1865, the Wesleyan Methodist Society built a meeting-house at the south end of Gibson Street. This building was severely plain as regards architecture, and is now an elementary school. In 1891, a modern artistic new church, from the plans of Mr Reavell, junior, of Alnwick, was built in High Street with a spacious school-room under the main building.

Previous to 1892, Alnwick was the circuit chapel, but at this date it was transferred to Amble, when the resident minister became the superintendent of the circuit, and the following Rev. gentlemen have filled this important office: Revs. Ralph Green, David Hay, J. Doubleday, J. S. Prior, W. Hunter, J. S. Halliday, D. Welsh, J. E. Eland, J. P. Yates, and the present minister the Rev. S. Snowden.

THE PRIMITIVE METHODISTS

This is the youngest religious body in Amble and first commenced public worship in

March 1885, in the old Drill Hall, eventually removing to the old Sale Rooms in Queen Street. Through a large amount of energy on the part of the small congregation a handsome new church was built in 1902 in Percy Street, near the harbour. For a good many years there was no resident minister, the mission being served by local preachers from the circuit. The first resident minister was J. W. Waddell followed by the following Rev. gentlemen: Revs. J. Hanley, A. Toyne, T. Alderson, J. Goodreid, M. Pattison, D. Goodwin, and B. Redhead, who is the present minister.

There is also a small body of Plymouth Brethren who hold services in the old Congregational Chapel, now the Masonic Hall. The Salvation Army have an iron building at the north end of Cross Street where they hold their indoor services.

VILLAGE SCHOOLS

The first school within the memory of one of Amble's oldest inhabitants, Mr James Rutherford, was held in a barn on the old "Causay" now a part of Gibson Street. In 1834, this place had done duty for at least a previous generation, and thus it takes us back to the village school of the eighteenth century.

The next school was held in one of the old cottages near the top of the Wynd. At this time there were four schools in Amble, viz. the one already mentioned, and another next door, one in Victoria Street, and the small cottage which formerly adjoined the Wellwood Arms was also a school house.

Later, in 1850, a school committee was formed, and a school opened in Queen Street. At a later date it was removed to Queen Street, north. In 1855, by public subscriptions and a grant of land from Mr Smith of Togston, a public school was provided by the side of the highway leading to the sea, and was long known as the "Lonnen School." By adding another story, thirty years later, the old school did duty down till 1909, and is now the Urban District Council Offices.

A Church of England School was provided in Queen Street in 1872, shortly after the building of the Parish Church. Twenty-seven years later, in 1899, the Medd Memorial Schools were provided by the same body to accommodate three hundred and thirty children, after an attempt to establish a School Board had failed by a ballot vote.

In 1879, the Roman Catholic School was commenced, and twelve years later, in 1891, the old Wesleyan Chapel was converted into an elementary school. This latter is now leased to the County Education Authority, and does duty as an infant's school.

For many years the "Lonnen School" where the parents of a passing generation received their scanty course of education, was getting sadly out of date as regards accommodation, besides many other requirements for the advanced paraphernalia of the present age.

The 1902 Education Act put the schools on the rates, and a movement was at once set on foot to provide new council schools. Eventually a site was secured at the west end of the town, on the way to Radcliffe. Splendid new schools with every requisite of an up-to-date character now fill the rôle of the old village school in the "sea Lonnen," with accommodation for three hundred children.

PUBLIC INSTITUTIONS—
READING-ROOMS, ETC.

The reading-room as an institution is indispensable to every village, and Amble in remote days had its reading-room. The most important of recent times was that which was held in a room of the premises, now Mr McInnes's shop, at the corner of Queen Street and Cross Street. There was a library in connection with this reading-room, which eventually formed the nucleus of the Parochial Library. This institution came to a close through lack of support twenty-five years ago.

The next attempt was in the Co-operative premises in Queen Street, where a reading-room was commenced during the great Northumberland miners' strike in 1887, but was soon discontinued, on account of the rapid extension of the Co-operative business.

Not to be denied, a disused photographic

studio was next requisitioned as a reading-room at the end of Cross Street, north.

Shortly after an attempt was made to provide a public Mechanics Institute, Mr H. Andrews offering to lend a sum of money free of interest; the rest of the capital it was proposed to provide by shares. This very laudable scheme fell through by sheer querulous opposition to petty details.

The old Assembly Rooms was then turned into a quasi-military institute under the Percy Artillery, controlled by the local members of that body. A reading and billiard-room combined was provided at one end of the hall. The other portion was used as a drill hall and gymnasium, and served a good purpose for a few years.

Amble now boasts of a very fine Social Club situated in Bede Street, built in 1902. It is a large and commodious building, containing bar, dining-room, and reading-room on the ground floor. The second floor contains a splendid billiard-room (two tables), games-room, and bathrooms. There is also a splendid reference library, and a membership of over four hundred.

A Mechanics Institute was erected in Middleton Street in 1903, comprising a large billiard-room, reading-room and library, and has a large membership.

About the same time a Church of England Young Men's Institute was provided in Dovecote through the enthusiastic zeal of the Rev. Mr Robson, the then curate.

SMUGGLING

A hundred years ago there was a good deal of smuggling on the Northumbrian Coast, and it is only reasonable to suppose that the people of Amble shared in the common practice of illicit traffic. The mouth of the Coquet between the sandhills saw many a cargo safely landed. But other schemes were adopted, and one which found most favour at that period was for the smuggled goods to be deposited on the rocks known as Hadstone Scars. A sharp look-out was kept, and the contraband goods were brought ashore at favourable opportunities.

Mr James Rutherford tells a story of how his grandfather was victimised by the smugglers. Having a field near the Bondicar Burn he stacked his hay crop on the field. A large illicit cargo having been deposited on the Scars and the excisemen safe for the night, the adventurers were successful in landing the contraband goods safe ashore.

For want of a better place to store the plunder a hole was burrowed in the haystack, into which the greater part was deposited, the remainder being buried in a manure heap close by.

" The best-laid schemes gang aft agley." Sufficient care had not been taken to cover up the tracks, and the lynx-eyed limb of the law noticed something unusual about the hay-rick, and consequently a little probing solved the mystery of the hidden spoil.

Then, as now, it was absolutely necessary that the guilt should be fixed on someone, and the unfortunate owner of the haystack was taken in charge, marched off to Wark-worth and lodged in the tower at the bridge end, where he remained until his explanation was considered satisfactory.

In another instance an unusually valuable cargo was landed near Hauxley, and an Amble man with a cart heavily laden with spirits, silk, etc., while making his way home in the grey dawn was espied by the revenue man. The race was all in favour of the man of law, who was on horseback, and the fugi-tive made up his mind quickly. Nearing where the Hope Railway Bridge now stands the driver overturned the coup cart from the shafts and wheels, and with the bales of silk mounted the horse's back and went off at the gallop. Expecting this to be the whole of the smuggled goods, and fearing that some-one might steal the kegs, the officer stood by the spoils he had safe, till the morning light, while the most valuable part of the cargo had escaped him.

Many similar stories are told reminiscent of the bygone lawless days when the spirit of adventure was a predominant feature in the character of the rude Northerner.

The extensive cellars at Gloster Hill old mansion are said to have been a great storage place for the smuggled goods. Besides, several houses in Amble had cellars attached, the existence of which was only known to a few. A notable instance of this secret cellar was discovered under the diminutive cottage near the top of the Wynd, with an outside approach, when the property came into the hands of the Richardson family at the beginning of last century.

At this time (1811) this same cot was the only retail beer house in the little hamlet.

THE VILLAGE INNS

With the introduction of the licensing laws at the beginning of the last century, the licensed victuallers took the place of the right to bake and brew, for which the tenants paid the Lord of the Manor six shillings annually.

As previously stated the small cottage at the top of the Wynd had this privilege in 1811, when the property changed hands. When this closed, the business of innkeeper was only a short distance removed, to the property now in the occupation of Mr J. T. Melrose, butcher, and for a few years Shanks' Queen's Head was the principal and only inn in the village. A little later James Innes built the Gardiner's Arms almost immediately opposite, and it is now the oldest public-house in the town. The Radcliffe Arms was the next in order, built by Walker together with the adjoining property, Walker's Yard.

The Mason's Arms at the corner of Broomhill Road came next, and then the Bluebell Inn, situate in "the Blue Bell Lonnen" now Albert Street. Then followed the Fox and Hounds at the foot of the Wynd, and then the Ship Inn in the "Sea Lonnen" now Church Street. This old inn is now the residence of Mr Joseph Thompson.

The Harbour Hotel was the first inn provided for the harbour end of the town, and during a delay in the construction of the harbour in 1842 the contractor built a block of buildings at the top of Queen Street which included the Waterloo Hotel. The Wellwood Arms, previously the farm-house for the Link House Farm, was turned into a public-house a little later, and the Togston Arms, now Mr McInnes's stationer's shop came next.

Another public-house was provided for the harbour end of the town, viz. the Schooner Inn, and during the construction of the Berwick-Newcastle Railway the Dock Hotel was built. Next came the Railway Inn, now the residence of Mr J. W. Beattie and the latest addition was the Steamboat Inn.

About twenty-five years ago a large and commodious hotel was built near the railway

station which, together with the Dock Hotel
and the Wellwood Arms Inn, recently re-
novated, are the principal establishments
which provide accommodation for visitors to
the town.

SHIPBUILDING

Shipbuilding in a small way was at one time carried on at Amble, and a small fleet of useful merchant ships was built and owned by people in Amble and district in the early 'Fifties. The rapid progress of steamships in the middle of the last century, however, nipped in the bud this infant industry.

The first ship recorded to have been built at Amble dates back to the end of the eighteenth century. About this time enormous quantities of oak trees were cut down in Chevington Wood, with the evident intention of replanting, which was never done, and from this timber a vessel was constructed on the Coquet banks near the old " granary " on the Warkworth road, and was named the *Chevington Oak*.

After the passing of the Harbour Act, 1837, shipbuilding was commenced on the Braid by a Mr Douglas of Sunderland. The first vessels built were the *Breeze*, *Aid* and *Landscape*.

With Mr Douglas came the late respected postmaster, Mr Thomas Leighton, and, in 1851, Messrs Leighton & Sanderson commenced shipbuilding on the river-bank, now occupied by the brickworks. In all this firm built seven ships, i.e. the *Perseverence*, *Providence*, *Isabella and Mary*, *Sunrise*, *Amble*, *Glorianna* and the *Agenora*, the last named being built in 1861. In 1868, another ship was built on the north side of the Coquet. A floating dock, which was of no practical use, was also built, and it ultimately went to pieces on the Braid.

The following is a list of ships which were owned by residents, some of which were regular traders to Amble till about twenty-five years ago.

ORIGINAL HARBOUR COMPANY.—
   Christina Murray, *Charles Molloy*, *Felix Ladbroke*, *Earl of Newborough*, *Sun*, *Sir J. Rennie*, *Sir H. Webb*, *Wee Tottie*, *Prince Saxe-Coburg*.

MESSRS RICHARDSON BROS.—
   Cedar, *Green Olive*, *Galilee*, *Kishon*, *Kedron*, *Radiant*, *Landscape*, *Star of Peace*, *Jane Brown*, *Chatteranga*, *Savannah-le-mer*, *Serepta*.

RUIN OF MANOR HOUSE, AMBLE.

[Photo by J. L. McAndrews.

COQUET ISLAND.

[*Photo by W. G. Chambers.*

Messrs Harrison & Henderson (*Fish Merchant*),—
Derwentwater, Sundew, Bonne Mer, Dove.

Mr John Henderson (*Gas Works*).—
Elizabeth Henderson, Helen Richards, *Auld Reekie*, Eastern Provence, Red Deer, Ailsa Craig.

Messrs Leighton & Sanderson.—
Providence, Perseverence, Amble, Coral Queen, Sunrise.

Messrs Hedley & Gibb.—
Jane, Isabella and Mary.

Mr J. H. Barrie.—
Lizzie Barrie, Caspian, Rosella, Wild Rose, Ceylon, Lyra.

Messrs Shotton & Calder.—
Glorianna, Agenora, Lancaster, Percy, Warkworth Castle, Sea Flower.

Mr T. Young.—
Isabella.

Mr Muers.—
Jane and Eleanor, Mentor, Abbotsford.

Mr Duncan.—
Lady Matheson, Protector, Wave Spirit.

Mr McInnes.—
Lebanon.

Mr R. Matthews.—
Huntley, Hiawatha.

Mr Hay.—
Hays.

Mr J. Turnbull.—
Halicore.

Mr J. Heatley.—
Humility.

Mr H. Andrews (*Broomhill Coal Co.*).—
Douse, Harebell, Lily, Nymphen, Wigeon, Clectra, Friendship, Inconstant, Mendora, Victoria, Cuba, Ceres, Stork, United, Union, Union T.

THE RAILWAY

Shortly after the completion of the harbour, the Newcastle and Berwick Railway Company applied for parliamentary powers to construct a railway to connect Amble by a branch line with the main line at Chevington.

For nearly thirty years this line was only used for mineral traffic—the coals from Broomhill Colliery being run to the harbour by the gradient of the line, and returned to the Colliery by means of horses.

With the development of Broomhill Colliery in the early 'Seventies and the consequent influx of people to the district, the Railway Company were induced to start passengers and goods service.

The formal opening took place on Whit Monday, 1879, when the first real passenger service was commenced. At the present time there is a fairly good train service on the line, viz. five trains out and five trains in, with special service on Saturdays, and frequent excursions. There is, however, no Sunday service.

Upwards of half a million tons of coal from Broomhill Colliery are conveyed over the branch annually to Amble Harbour, besides a fairly large goods traffic.

Up to 1894 there was only a single line, and the Broomhill Coal Company found their traffic so congested that application was made to Parliament for power to construct a new railway.

As a result, an agreement was made with the North Eastern Railway Company to double the existing line from Broomhill to Amble, and this was completed in the above year.

A few years later the opening of Togston Colliery so delayed the Broomhill traffic that the Coal Company provided a new, independent line for their own use, connecting up the Radcliffe Colliery line at the old pit.

By arrangement, however, the Broomhill coals are still carried over the North Eastern Line.

For many years rumours have filled the

air of a new coast line route, which recently has been given some credence by the opening out of the new mining enterprises at Woodhorn, Newbiggen, and Creswell.

THE COQUET

The Coquet for ever, the Coquet for aye,
  The Coquet the king of the stream and the brae,
From his high mountain throne to his bed in the sea,
  Oh where shall we find such a river as thee.

Then blessings be on him and long may he glide,
  The fisherman's home and the fisherman's pride,
From Harden's green hill to old Warkworth sae gray,
  The Coquet for ever, the Coquet for aye.

—HARBOTTLE.

The king of Northumbrian streams on its
course from the Scottish border to the sea,
passes through lovely sylvan scenery, by
heathery bank and flowery brae, but loses all
its picturesqueness in the vicinity of Amble,
and becomes only a subject for the topo-
grapher, the geologist, or the engineer.
    The low-lying marshy flat which occupies
the intervening space between Amble and
Warkworth is a bleak, treeless waste, and to
a close observer gives the impression that
centuries of Coquet floods have brought down

plenty of alluvial matter to fill up what seems
to have been a prehistoric lake.   This theory
may be doubted, but certain it is that at some
period or other the river has flowed over
every yard of this low-lying land.   The
original course of the river seems to have
been to hug the Magdaline fields on the west
side of the flat, turning east by Gloster Hill
and close by the old Manor House to the site
of the brickworks, then turning north by
Helsay Point between the sandhills, and
forming an outlet half a mile north of the
present mouth.

It is just possible that if the Coquet had
not ceased its winding proclivities in 1764,
and made a bee-line for the sea Amble would
have remained an obscure village.   When
the flood made a new outlet the course was
straight east, from the brickworks past the
Radcliffe staithes to the east end of Leazes
Street, and still keeping to the original curve
again flowed north to a point west of the
present harbour mouth.   Old Father Coquet's
frequent changing of his course was for ages
a continuous source of trouble to the land-
owner on either side in the lower reaches,
and inquisitions were often held to settle dis-
putes caused by the river changing the land-

marks in its erratic course through the sand-
hills to the sea. Until recently metal pillars
marked the course of the old river channel
by way of Leazes Street, but the fish dock
and streets of houses occupy the space where
the Coquet flowed in days gone by, before
Amble had a harbour.

Many generations of anglers have sung the
praises of the Coquet as the fisherman's pride,
but their praise does not apply to the Coquet
in the immediate vicinity of Amble. Midway
between Amble and Warkworth there is a
good deal of rod fishing, and at certain
seasons of the year as a rule there is good
sport.

The Coquet has always been a salmon
river, but for many years real salmon (*Salmo
saler*) in the Coquet were as rare as black
swans.

Many reasons have been assigned for the
cause, which were mostly conjectures. By
some it was asserted that the building of the
great dam at Acklington in 1778, had driven
the salmon out of the Coquet. Others that
it was the great increase of the bull trout
(*Salmo eriox*,) and its proclivities for destroying the salmon fry, while there were others
who blamed the harbour works. This idea

that the bull trout was the cause became so conclusive that there was a determined attempt to exterminate the supposed intruder, and enormous numbers were destroyed at the locks at Warkworth Mill in the year 1865.

The attempt was a miserable failure, and it is asserted that in the following autumn the bull trout came up in greater numbers than ever known before. Time, the great adjuster has proved that the reasons assigned for the absence of real salmon from the Coquet were all pure hypotheses, for at the present time there is recorded to be about equal numbers of real salmon and bull trout taken from the river, while all the supposed reasons attributed for the absence of the real salmon from the Coquet remain in evidence.

The net fishing in the tideway from the harbour mouth to the Warkworth Mill is the exclusive right of the Duke of Northumberland. The same gentleman owns what is known as the "stell fishery" extending from the Bondicar Burn to the Grey Stone of Helsay, a point half a mile north of the harbour. This means that the right to fish with a net at low-water mark for this distance, about three miles, is also the exclusive right of the Duke of Northumberland, who has recently proved his title in the Courts.

One thing only is lacking to add to the fame of Father Coquet, viz. that with the exception of assisting in the construction of a harbour the only industry on its banks is coal mining, but let us hope the day is not far distant when there will be more than one industry to add to the mercantile fame of the Coquet.

NEW HALL AND HOPE HOUSE

The farms now known as New Hall and Hope House each half a mile distant, have always been part of the Manor of Ambell, and were the monastery lands lying to the west of the small hamlet.

Hope House, which consisted of five farms of land, ultimately became included in the Radcliffe estates, together with the manorial rights in Amble, Hauxley, and Togston Moor House (now Low Hall).

New Hall with its three farmholds was originally in the tenancy of a family named Wilson, and it was ultimately conveyed to Catherine Wilson, spinster in the year 1650, for the sum of £300 by Horsely who had bought portions of the previously confiscated lands from the Crown. The aforesaid Catherine Wilson married John Thompson, Rector of Bothal and two years later the farmholds were sold to Edward Cook who married an heiress, and so acquired land in Togston.

The name New Hall is accredited to the new mansion built here by Cook after he bought the estate. This imposing mansion-house stood in the field to the east of the farm steading, and was pulled down some time between 1833 and 1844.

From 1652, New Hall was retained in the Cook family, till it passed, by an heiress, to Isaac Cookson, who sold it to James Dand of Hauxley in the year 1833.

On the decease of the latter it was divided between his two sons. The western portion, which includes the farm steading, went to Mr James Dand, and the eastern portion to Mr Robert Dand of Gloster Hill. The portion adjoining Amble was bounded by the fence on the north of the new cemetery, but has now merged into the Gloster Hill estate.

GLOSTER HILL

THIS small township, although entirely independent of Amble, is to all intents and purposes a part of Amble, being almost a continuation of the town from the foot of the Wynd. Situated to the west of Amble, on the same ridge or bank of the old river-bed, and comprising in all two hundred and twelve acres, the whole one fine farm of good arable and pasture land.

There is a touch of old-time history round this place, and the visitor is struck by the ruined but extensive pillars which form a gateway to what must have been at one time a pretentious mansion. The outward view of the present house gives the impression as being only the remains of something better, and in reality is only part of the old-time mansion destroyed by fire in 1759. An old record states that " on Sunday a fire broke out at Gloucester Hill Seat house near Warkworth, which consumed it in a few hours.

One of the maid servants in saving her clothes, which she did by throwing them out of ye window was burnt in returning down stairs. It happened when ye family were at Church half a mile distant."

The interior still contains a good deal of its old peculiarities, such as a stone staircase, vaulted cellar, etc. There are very fine gardens adjoining the old hall, but are now let as sale gardens, together with a small cottage close by. The farm cottages are comparatively recent, and are some distance away from the old-time cottages near the Mansion House, which are now in a ruinous condition. The population of this puny township for the past hundred years has been practically stationary, having twenty-one souls in 1801 and thirty-nine in 1901, in the intervening years having once reached forty-six in 1861.

The historical side of Gloster Hill claims some antiquity from the Roman altar found here in 1856. This rare antiquarian relic was turned out when ploughing a field west of the farm steading near the road leading from the New Hall to Warkworth. The slab or altar stone measures eighteen inches by fourteen and bears the accredited inscription:

"*Martibus compestibus cohors prima*" the literal translation runs: "An altar dedicated to the sylvan mother by the first cohort." A similar altar to the same deity has been found on the Roman Wall near Benwell. It is naturally assumed that there was a small camp somewhere near, but no trace can be found, neither are there any traces of a road in the vicinity, which is strange, as Roman roads are so easily located in other parts of Northumberland on account of the vegetation turning brown in very dry weather.

This might be accounted for by the stones forming the road having sunk in the boulder clay to a big depth, so that sufficient soil has accumulated to keep the vegetation from feeling the lack of moisture in dry summers. At any rate no trace has yet been found, although the straight line west is and has been under close observation for some time past.

In the palmy days of Newminster Abbey, Roger Fitz Richard, Baron of Warkworth, amongst other grants to the monks about the middle of the twelfth century gave the abbot the right to make salt in the Geldean Burn. The site of these said salt works can be traced by the side of the burn immediately below the old farm-house. There appears to have been a shallow miniature lake which spring tides would fill, and salt could be made by natural evaporation. The low-lying marshy land known as the "Goatses" and according to some authorities the term is derived from a narrow cavern or inlet of the sea. Just here the Geldean Burn forms the inlet, and when the course of the river was down the Gut, by the highway, the tides would flow a long way up the burn and cover the marshy flat now known as the "Goatses."

From early in the twelfth century Gloster Hill has been the glebe land of the Rectory of Warkworth, granted to the Bishop of Carlisle by Henry I. It was the custom to let the glebe lands, tithes, etc., on lease for twenty-one years, renewable every seven years.

At the end of the seventeenth century it was held on lease by a member of the Lawson family, who seems to have been a real philanthropist and a benefactor of the entire district.

He rebuilt the village cross at Warkworth, gave a clock to the Parish Church; he likewise built a town house which contrived a double debt to pay, acting as a public meeting-place and a school house for the village.

The old historian, Warburton, writing in 1715, during this gentleman's tenure:

"Gloster Hill ye seat of George Lawson, Gent. is pleasantly situated on rising ground near ye sea, where is a woollen manufacture where are made broadcloths,   druggets where is employed some   of poor indigent persons about thirty are employed in   looms belonging to ye Dean and Chapter of Carlisle." *

Seeing that no trace of any such buildings are to be found other authorities assume that the mill was in Amble, one of the many benevolent schemes of the said George Lawson. Next to the imposing mansion the gardens seem to have been an extremely interesting feature, as Horsley writes, "the gardens are reconned very good and are much enquired after by travellers."

These gardens are certainly pleasantly situated on a gentle slope to the south, but have now lost a good deal of their splendour, and there is now an air of commercialism

* "Words above are missing in original."

which is in strong contrast with the description in the following advertisement of the period taken from the Newcastle *Courant* of that date.

"To let or sold against May Day next, Closter Hill estate belonging to Mr George Lawson, lying in the County of Northumberland nigh Warkworth, being leasehold for twenty-one years, renewable every seven, under the annual rent of £53, 4s. payable to the Bishop of Carlisle, and the lease renewed but a year ago, a very good and well-situated mansion-house within half a mile of the sea, with handsome gardens on the south and east of the house, a pleasant long terrace walk laid with gravel in the south garden, with many other agreeable grass walks, and planted with the choicest fruit trees of most kinds and plentiful bearers, a dovecote and a bowling green on advanced ground, with delightful prospect of the sea, exceedingly good out conveniences of stabling, a coach-house, barn, and byers, fold garths, a stackyard, and cottage houses, all contiguous and convenient to the estate; it being tythe free and nearly divided into closures with quick-set hedges in fine order and well watered in all seasons of the year, the whole is a complete method of husbandry, arable meadow and pasture."

There can be little doubt that Gloster Hill of that time was a model farm. At least, so it would appear, yet it does not seem to have found a purchaser, for the benevolent George Lawson died six years later, and was buried in Warkworth Church in the year 1738.

Six years later Gloster Hill was again advertised for sale and was acquired by Watson of Newton-by-the-Sea. Afterwards it passed to Purvis of Bedlington.

About the year 1770 it was leased to Robert Dand, formerly of Bedlington, and at a later date this family became the owners of the Glebe Farm. It is still retained in the Dand family, and the present owner is Robert Dand of Heckley Hall.

COQUET ISLAND

In an almost straight line east of Amble, and little over a mile from the land stands the little "eland of Cocket" as it is described by old chronicles.

Its whitewashed buildings, its towering lantern in a wide expanse of azure blue, makes it a most attractive piece of seascape on which the eye lovingly lingers. From the island there is a most extensive view of coast-line and interior. In the foreground is Amble and its busy harbour, Warkworth Castle the last grim relic of feudalism, the beautiful sylvan valley of the Coquet with Simonside's towering escarpments forming a background to a charming picture.

Away to the north is Alnmouth Bay with Boulmer's rugged headland, the scene of many a shipwreck, and away in the distance is Dunstanborough's frowning ruin. To the south-west are the busy scenes of industry, colliery villages, and tall chimney stacks emitting dense volumes of smoke—an indisputable sign of industrial activity.

Simultaneous with the building of the harbour a lighthouse was built on the island, and the first light was exhibited in 1841. The lantern tower is eighty feet high from the water edge, and is built on the edge of the old fortalice of the monks. It is now an occulting light and flashes every three seconds.

The ruins of the old monastic institution can now only be traced in the base of the lantern tower and built into the present cottages.

The island is fourteen acres in extent, all grass, with the exception of the lightkeeper's garden patches. The grass is coarse, consequently no cattle or sheep are to be found grazing on its bitter pasture.

It was at one time a famous rabbit warren, and the breed of the white Angora rabbit was introduced by the Duke of Northumberland as an experiment, but was a failure, and the rabbits disappeared with the building of the lighthouse. With this also disappeared the natural history side of the island, and instead of it being the home of the eider duck, the tern, and numerous gulls,

H

they are all now conspicuous by their absence. Seals used to visit the island a good deal, but at the present time they are rare visitors.

At one time Coquet Island was a great resort for holiday crowds, not only from the mainland, but steam-boat trips landed crowds from Tyneside.

At the present time the island is not so popular with pleasure-seekers as it used to be, and the cycle, the motor, or cab for a run in the country is preferred to a boating trip to Coquet Island.

There are three landing-places, one on the north known as the Quayhole, and the other two on the south are known as the Horse Haven and the Ducket Hole. The Horse Haven is partly made, and is supposed to be the one mentioned in the lease of quarries on the island, which stipulated that the lessee spend a sum of money in providing a landing-place for the small craft which then traded to and from the island.

The entire population consists of the families of the three lighthouse keepers.

The history of Coquet Island is especially interesting, and takes us back to early Saxon times—the dawn of Christianity in the North of England. Bede speaks of the island as being celebrated for the concourse of monks during the conversion of Northumberland from barbarism to the light of faith.

In 684, the saintly Cuthbert left his lonely cell on the outer Farnes to grant an interview to the Abbess of Whitby, the sister of King Elfried and on pressure foretold the early death of her king brother and the ultimate succession of her other reputed brother Aldred, then on a course of study in the island of Scotts. The abbess knew that Elfried wished to make the holy man Bishop against his will, and to her he reluctantly admitted that he would submit to the dignity that was being forced upon him, but in two years he himself would be dead. Strange, but true, this prophecy was fulfilled to the letter.

Like Amble and included in the same grant Coquet Island was given to the Tyne-mouth Priory monks by Robert Mowbray It seems to have fallen into the old order of things after the Conquest, as it still remained a monastic institution down to the dissolution of the monasteries in 1536. There is record of a hermit cell here in the twelfth century, for buried at Tynemouth lies Henry the Hermit of Coquet Isle. The legend of Coquet from the chronicles of Tynemouth Priory taken from the County History, owing to the quaint description of the holy man and his ways may be of interest.

" The hermit was a Dane of noble birth and he was said to have been directed by a vision to make good his escape from a marriage his parents were endeavouring to force upon him, and to serve God all his days on this penitent rock. He landed at Tynemouth and obtained the priors' consent to build a small cell on the island, which was in charge of one monk. For some years he allowed himself a little loaf and a draught of water every day, and afterwards he took food only thrice a week and gave up speaking for three years. During the last four years of his life he ground his barley into meal with a millstone, and after moistening it with water made it into little round cakes which he dried in the sun.

" His privations brought upon him many harsh words and opprobrious epithets from the monk in charge of the island. His relations sent to urge his return to Denmark, pointing out that there were plenty of wild

spots there suitable for a hermitage. He
threw himself on his knees before a crucifix
and believed that he heard Christ command
him to remain to the end in his Northumbrian
cell. He regarded a loathsome affliction on
one of his knees as a further sign forbidding
his departure. Supporting himself with a
crutch he still insisted on digging his little
field, his crops were marvellous. Like Saint
Cuthbert he was credited with second sight.
The monk, his prosecutor, found him praying
before the high altar for the soul of his half-
brother of whose murder in Denmark he had
a presentiment that was well founded.

"Another day as some merchantmen were
sailing smoothly past he said to one of the
numerous visitors that hermits usually attract
'Do you not see the monster following those
ships.' They then perceived the figure of a
woman gliding on the clouds on the sea.
'That woman,' he continued, 'will presently
strike the sea and raise a storm that will en-
gulf the vessels and most of their crews.'
Before long came the news that the ships had
been driven on the sands and rocks, nearly
all hands being lost.

"We are not told that the saint essayed to
exorcise the fatal phantom; a mariner subse-

quently ascribed his escape from shipwreck to Saint Henry's intercession. A drunken monk of Tynemouth was dumbfounded when the hermit named the place and hour of his last debauch.   A priest in the immediate neighbourhood was lying dangerously ill, and as Saint Henry approached his house he heard the demons gloating over the sure possession of his soul, alleging the priest had only done one good thing in his life. With difficulty he convinced them that the one good deed was of such a nature as to outweigh all the bad ones. Such was their disappointment that the demons placed no further hindrance in the way of the priest's recovery and reformation.   Except for a pilgrimage to Durham to the shrine of the saint he strove to emulate, this is the only mention of Saint Henry quitting the island.

"In the winter 1126-27, the pain caused by his ulcerated knee became intense, but Saint Henry would not allow anyone to enter his cell. He passed the cold days and nights all alone without fire or light with cheerful contentment. On Sunday 16th of January a man on the island thought he heard two choirs of angels chanting alternate verses of the 'Te Deum.'   The hymn ceased, the hermit's bell rang, the monk of the island hastened to the cell and found Saint Henry seated on a stone holding the bell rope in all the calm of sleep—life had passed away. A mortuary candle that the saint had no means of lighting was burning at his side. After a very necessary ablution the body acquired the whiteness of snow. The parishioners were determined to place it in a shrine in their own church, no doubt at Warkworth. As they were conveying it to the mainland a thick fog lowered over the sea and they lost their way. They landed near another church, perhaps that of Woodhorn, in which the body rested that night. Saint Henry, it was declared, now appeared in a vision and directed that it should be carried to Tynemouth the first thing the next morning, before the neighbours had had time to reassemble and defend what they regarded as their precious heritage. At Tynemouth the monks buried it with all honour a little to the south of Saint Oswin's shrine."

A century later there was another hermit on the island, but, from what we can gather, of an entirely different frame of mind, and from miracles and second sight Martin seems to have turned to mechanics, and constructed a windmill to grind his corn. This was not an age of progress and the hermit's windmill raised the ire of the mighty Baron of Warkworth, who was amongst other things the owner of the parish mill. This seeming rivalry to the lord's mill could not be tolerated, and landing on the island with thirty men armed with mattocks and axes they wantonly threw down the mill, the result of the labour and genius of the holy man. In fact, through the protest of his servant against the destruction of the mill, the hermit nearly lost his life. It is also stated that many people of that day thought it was not the right thing for a professed hermit to speculate in a windmill, as mills, like other shows, were apt to harbour promiscuous company. From this it seems that the all-powerful baron, not content with owning the land and other privileges, rose in his might and denied the holy man the right to grind his own corn with the aid of his own genius by inventing a windmill.

In 1415, there was a small fortalice " Turris-de-Cocketland " reported as belonging to the Prior of Tynemouth, in all probability provided as a sort of refuge in troublesome times, and is now the base of the lighthouse.

At the dissolution of the monasteries the last monk, Thomas Bennet, the then chaplain seems to have fallen into the new order of things, Vicar of Bray fashion, and continued to farm the revenues for the Crown, which amounted to £15, 4s. 8d. made up as follows:

" The farm of the island, which contained fourteen acres of pasture with buildings and a chapel on the island, and a tenement, a barn, and three sections of arable land in the village of Hauxley, a rent charge issuing out of Warkworth Castle, a tenement called Donkin Rig, leased to the widow of Edward Fenwick of Rothley, a cottage and garden at Seaton in the Parish of Woodhorn, a cottage at Ellington, a cottage at Meresfen, a cottage at Newbiggen formerly worth 4s. but now worth nothing, a rent from two mills at Warkworth in the tenure of Sir Edward Radcliffe, a cottage and lands at Hart in the County of Durham in the tenure of the Vicar of Tynemouth, tenant at will of the King, a cottage and two acres of land at Westoe in the County of Durham, making altogether the aforementioned rent-roll."

The island and other manorial privileges were granted by the great despoiler Henry VIII. to Dudley, Earl of Warwick, afterwards Duke of Northumberland, and on his attainder for treason it again reverted to the Crown. James I. granted it to George Salter and John Wilkinson, who sold it to Edward Corley and Robert Morgan, gentlemen, of London. Afterwards it was sold to Sir William Bowes of Strethlem, who leased it to Francis Jessop and others for twenty-one years, reserving the right to dig stone and take it away in ships for his own use. He also made a covenant that the lessees shall expend £150 in making a dock or small haven for ships in some part of the said island. Also the lessor, after the lessees had recouped themselves £400 to have one-third of the yearly gains from the stone in the island and reserved power to re-enter if the lessees in any one year should take less than five hundred tons. The stone was of exceptional good quality, and large quantities were shipped annually, including stone to repair the battlements of Syon House.

We again find the island to have changed hands in 1675, having been sold by Sir William Bowes's grandson, William, Earl of old Elvet, to David Main of Newcastle, who resold it to John Kelly of Chevington, from whom it passed to Robert Widdrington of Hauxley. In 1753, the island came into the possession of the Duke of Northumberland, but the land at Hauxley was retained in the Widdrington family. It is now leased to the Masters and Brethren of Trinity House.

Coquet Island seems not only to have been the home of saints but also to some extent of sinners. After the attainder of Dudley, the kingmaker, the island again became the property of the Crown, when it became the resort of lawless men and coiners. A good many of these coins called "hardheads" were struck, but, fortunately, they seem to have been a failure. "After the space of twenty days could not bring to any perfection and having made to the value of £10 they gave it up." After this the report goes on to say that the parties swore on a book that they should never use that art again. An accomplice was the Captain of Wark, named Rowland Forster, who gave evidence on examination two years later.

Certainly not the least important event in the history of Coquet Island is the part played in the Civil War of the Commonwealth. From the resort of lawbreakers it eventually became a military station, and felt all the thunders of war. In 1644, the Scots having invaded the north and east of Northumberland with 20,000 men, according to old records, Colonel Curset, Commander of the Scots army reported:—" They have taken the Isle of Cocket and the garrison thereof with seventy commanders and common soldiers and seven pieces of ordnance and all the ammunition, and have placed a garrison of their own thereon." This very meagre report of the occupation gives no account of the method of attack, whether by raising the siege or by surprise. Neither is there a list of casualties, and we are forced to the conclusion that the battle of Coquet Island was a case of caught napping and that it was a bloodless capture. Neither are we furnished with any account of the evacuation.

According to Leyland in 1528, " the Isle of Coquit standeth upon a good veyne of secoals and at the ebb men digge them on the shore by the clives and cliffs and find very good." Later years have disproved the old historian and " the very good veyne of coal " is the outcropping edge of a poor seam outside the real coalfield. There seems, however, to have been a good deal of coal digging here. Horsley writes in 1730, "that the island was uninhabited"; but seventeen years later another writer states, "there was huts for diggers of secoal of which here is great plenty."

Doubtless the primitive mining, like the pits on the mainland opposite, was chiefly for salt making, of which there are records; and traces of pits and salt pans still on the island.

Another writer, Wallis, in 1769, gives a faithful description of the island.

"The island is a mile in circumference and a mile and a quarter from the mainland, stored with rabbits. It hath pit coal as mentioned by Leland, also white freestones and slate, the former of different fineness, the worst with some molecular, the latter usually about threequarters of an inch thick. On the west side have been salt pans, about sixty yards from which are the ruins of the monastic cell and chapel, and just below them is a bank of factitious sand of remarkable brightness, the dissolution of silvery ragstone, of which there are large strata between Warkworth and Alnmouth, often left bare after storms and high tides. Hard by, on a rock, grows plenty of rape, possibly brought there by some shipwreck."

Another description of the island issued by the Admiralty in 1685 will be of interest to mariners.

"Cocket Island lieth six leagues from Tynemouth Castle and about a mile off shore, and in a good road for southerly winds. From the south end of the island to the shore it is all rock and broken ground when at low water. At one place there is only eight or nine feet, and dangerous; but the north side is bold, only from the north-west part of the island lie of some rocks about half a mile; small vessels may bring the island south and anchor in three or four fathoms at low water, this road is clean sand."

A still more interesting account is from a Dutch book and copied from the County History.

" The Cocker Island is a very little island and not high; it lieth about a league from the land and you may come to an anchor in it for an east-south and south-east wind, but the wind comming into the northwards of the coast maketh this a bad road. For you must lye betwixt the island and the mainland, where you have no shelter from a north wind. On the south side of the island the ground is foul, and a little to the southwards of the island runneth off a foul ledge of rocks from the shore until athwart the island.

"He that cometh from the southwards must keep the coast of Bamborough without the island or else he should not fail to saile upon the point of the aforesaid ledge. Betwixt the ledge and the island it is very narrow so that a man standing at low-water mark upon the rocks of the ledge should almost be able to cast with a stone to the island. For to saile in there take heed to the marks hereafter discribed. There standeth a house upon the sea side which is a salt kettle, and also a Castle somewhat further in within the land which doeth show itself high."

As previously stated in all the navigation reports, at the south end of the island there is a broad stretch of jagged rocks connecting the island with Hauxley on the mainland. There are stories told that at a comparatively recent date it was possible to walk to the island by this narrow channel, but history discounts this fable, as the survey of 1682 gives eight or nine feet of water at low tide.

HAUXLEY

THE little village of "Auxley" as it was called in "ye olden times" is of the ordinary type of village with houses on either side of the highway. There is only a few houses left, but there is evidence of Hauxley once being a substantial village.

Situated on a rising eminence it commands an extensive land and sea view to the south and east, besides a beautiful view of the uplands to the west, terminating in the Simonside Hills. At the eastern extremity of the little village stands the residence of Mr J. T. Dand, known as Hauxley Cottage, which makes no pretence at architecture, but, nestling in a quiet nook with a splendid outlook, gives it an old-world charm.

Close by is the only trace of the old mansion-house of the Widdringtons, so long identified with Hauxley, in the conspicuous doorhead of a low cottage with the date

1600, besides other fragments of massive mouldings included in the walls of the old cottages.

On the south side of the road passing through the village stands Hauxley Hall, a rather imposing mansion. Standing amongst a clump of trees with extensive gardens and park-like pastures stretching away to the south. This was originally the residence of the Kirton family, who held large possessions in the locality. The Kirton estate came into the possession of the Widdrington family in 1672, and to them is attributed the south extension to the original building, the laying-out of the extensive gardens, the park pastures, tree planting, etc., which gives a special charm to this part of Hauxley.

On the south side of the highway, and now forming part of the garden wall, are traces of the fishermen's dwellings which originally made Hauxley a busy village. About thirty years ago the fishermen were provided with a new village, half a mile distant on the sea-shore, known as Hauxley Sea-houses, where once stood the farm steading of the Kirton family. A good many stories are told of the peculiar revelries, practical jokes, etc., of the past generation of Hauxley fishermen in their

village inn, now re-constructed into a pretty
cottage.

The Manor of Hauxley was included with
Amble and Coquet Island in the grant by the
Conqueror's henchman Richard-de-Mowbray
to the Convent and Priory of Tynemouth in
1126. The grant was further confirmed by
Richard Cœur de Lion previous to setting
out for the Holy Land and also by King John
in 1203. All the land and other privileges
of the Manor were held by tenants and copyholders of the priory, some ultimately becoming freeholders.

In all the revenue of the priory in 1328
amounted to £18, 7s. 2d. a year.

In the middle of the fourteenth century the
powerful Baron, Sir Gerard Widdrington,
whose possessions adjoined the priory lands
began to dispute the prior's claim to the
Manor of Hauxley and began to exert his own
claims in a rather peculiar manner by tortur-
ing some Austin Friars which he took to be
monks of the priory. Besides, the cruel man
did not scruple to attempt the prior's life.
These were the days of trial by combat, and
a day was appointed to prove the rival claims
in the lists. At the intervention of Lady
Mary Percy, wife of Henry Percy, Baron of

Alnwick, Sir Thomas Colville, a valiant knight, was induced to enter the lists as the prior's champion in mortal combat to make good his claim. But the report says that "all were struck with astonishment at the unexpected appearance and boldness of the stranger knight who had won renown in the French Wars, so that the Widdringtons dare not oppose him," and the Hauxley lands were from this time the undisputed property of the priory down to the dissolution of the monasteries in 1536.

At the dissolution, the whole of the priory's possessions reverted to the Crown. John Widdrington, who previously acted as bailiff for the priory, acted in a similar capacity for the Crown, and presented in the returns, rents from the eleven copyholders amounting to £19, 0s. 7d. besides 10d. for pannage of swine, 26s. 8d. for four cobles used for fishing, and 6s. for assize of "bread and ale"— in all £20, 14s. 1d.

The Hauxley Manor was in the possession of the Crown for nearly a hundred years, and was from time to time let on lease, at the previously stated rental. In 1628, Charles I. sold the Hauxley estates to one Bitchfield and others in order to raise money. Afterwards it was sold to Sir William Hewitt who resold it to Brown and Palfrey; Sir William Fenwick who previously bought the Manorial rights reserving the coal mines, etc.

It will be noticed that the transactions in the sale of land are the same as in the sister hamlet of Ambell—the original purchasers in each case being the same. Brown and Palfrey seem to have acted for the tenants of the holdings of the several parcels of land included in the purchase. In 1663, all the land in the township was held by the following—Robert Widdrington, Nichol Lewn, William Kirton, William Carr, John Clark, John Hudson and Robert Hall.

From this time onward the small holders were from time to time bought out and included in the Widdrington estates with the exception of Clark's freehold, which at a later date became the property of Edward Werge of Horton Glendale. This gentleman, some time previous, had acquired, after the Chancery suit, the Amble portion of the Widdrington estates. Werge afterwards sold the whole estates to Mr James Dand formerly of Bedlington, and it now comprises, with the exception of the Amble parcels of land, the very fine farm—Amble Moor House. The freehold in the name of Nicholas Lewn passed to the Radcliffe estates, and was known as the Hauxley fields.

The Widdringtons of Hauxley claimed to be the lineal descendants of the proud and powerful Baron of Widdrington of Norman blood, who so ignominiously failed to make good his claims by strength of arms to the Hauxley lands. Yet Hauxley came into the possession of the family, after the main line for their part in the unfortunate "Fifteen" had been blotted out.

John Widdrington the last of the male line died at Hauxley in 1797, without issue, but willed his possessions to his nieces Sarah Brown and Sarah Teasdale, with the injunction to take the name of Widdrington. Owing, however, to his speculations as a merchant previously in Newcastle, on his decease his estates were thrown into Chancery.

They were eventually released in 1809, but at the considerable cost of about half the estate, comprising the Amble portion. Sarah Brown married the Rev. Joseph Cook of Newton-on-the-Moor and Sarah Teasdale married Captain Tinling. The portion of Hauxley accruing to the Tinling-Widdrington succession was eventually sold to Captain S. E. Widdrington, son of the Rev. Cook and Sarah Brown, and their family, together with Mr Dand, now own the ancient Manor of Hauxley.

As previously stated a new fishing village was provided by Captain Widdrington. The new fishermen's quarters consist of modern stone-built, commodious cottages, situate on the Links close to a sandy beach, which affords every facility for the fisherman's calling.

The sanitary conditions are excellent, and the landlord spares no pains nor expense to make it a model fishing village. These toilers of the deep are encouraged, entertained, and fêted in every way by an indulgent landlord no doubt anxious that this old-time industry may not die out.

RADCLIFFE COLLIERY

This small colliery village now comprises the principal portion of the population of the township of Hauxley, and dates from the year 1836. Out of courtesy to the owners of the Royalties being descendants from the illustrious line which ended with the unfortunate Earl of Derwentwater in 1715, the new mining village was given the name of Radcliffe.

Situate on a low-lying flat, with little natural drainage, and houses of a bad, old-fashioned back-to-back type, with ground floor and loft, no sewerage system, and streets made up of small coals and mud, roughly sums up the conditions of old Radcliffe. Until comparatively recent times this was the very ordinary sanitary conditions of colliery villages in the North of England, and Radcliffe was no exception to the general rule.

This condition of affairs is now happily changed, and the Radcliffe Colliery village of to-day will compare favourably, both as to housing, sanitary conditions, water supply, etc., with any other colliery village in the North of England. Several new rows of up-to-date houses have been built, and the old slums have been converted into substantial workmen's dwellings with up-to-date modern requirements.

The original owner very magnanimously provided a spacious building in the centre of the village, and a stone tablet set forth the following inscription.

"This building was erected by Messrs Ladbroke & Brown for the education and religious instruction of the workmen and children of Radcliffe Colliery, A.D. 1842."

The use of the building for religious instruction the donor expected would be taken up by the incumbent of the Parish of Warkworth, but as the then rector did not avail himself of this opportunity to minister to the spiritual needs of the new community the right to use the building for religious purposes was granted to a small Wesleyan Methodist body, who worshipped in the old place for half a century, in fact until the building got into a very dilapidated condition. The services for a short time were conducted in the new Co-operative Public Hall, and in 1893, a new Wesleyan Methodist Chapel was opened. Meanwhile the school for education purposes became totally unfit for use, and new schools, with a small building for religious observances of the members of the Church of England, were provided by the untiring zeal of the Rev. James Fairbrother, Vicar of Amble. The small church was dedicated to the Good Shepherd, and together with the schools was opened for public use on January 6th, 1894.

The school accommodation a few years later again became inadequate, and handsome new schools were provided by the County Council. When the educational needs were provided for elsewhere, the old school with some repairs became a reading-room or library for the village youths, and still in a measure fulfilled the intention of the donors.

At the renovation of Radcliffe by the present owners, Broomhill Collieries Ltd., a new Mechanics Institute was provided, and the old place, which had for over half a century faithfully fulfilled the work for which it was intended, was eventually turned into a modern cottage.

In 1892, extensive co-operative premises vided in 1893, and it is needless to add that the religious needs of Radcliffe are well provided for.

In 1892, extensive co-operative premises which included shops for carrying on a large business, and a public lecture hall were built, which, together with a very fine Workmen's Social Club, have added considerably to the social side of Radcliffe village.

After the colliery was opened, as previously stated, in 1836, the houses for workmen were built in sections as the workings extended, and it was a common occurrence for families to remove in as soon as the roof was put on; windows and doors they were willing to wait for. In those days the fire-grate, oven, etc., were part of the furniture, and they were fixed so that they could be taken away at the shortest notice.

In the early days of Radcliffe Colliery there was a great deal of migration between Shilbottle and Radcliffe, and very few interchanges on the part of the colliers of the southern part of the country. Radcliffe was in the great county strike of 1844, and suffered all the privations, the usual result of strikes, but infinitely worse before the days of militant trade unionism.

The Radcliffe men were evicted, and supplanted by "blacklegs" from Cornwall. The usual eviction scenes were enacted, some were passive spectators, others vigorous resisters, while some fortified their houses and resisted with all the tenacity of despair. The Green Lane leading to the Hope Farm was the principal camping-ground of the evicted families. The miners' wives took it upon themselves to intimidate the blacklegs, and the Cornishmen were serenaded to and from the colliery by the women-folk. This unfriendly attention seems to have had a much better effect than mob opposition, for the blacklegs cleared out after a short stay.

Three years later there was another strike, this time a local affair, and more evictions. This strike only lasted six weeks, and originated in a dispute by the miners objecting to the system of weighing then in use at the colliery. A settlement was effected by having one tub in four weighed and strike an average, and this arrangement was carried out until six years later, in 1853, when it was enacted that all hewers' tubs pass over the weigh.

In the year 1855, the colliery, together with the interest in the harbour, passed out of the hands of the originally Colliery-Harbour Company and was purchased by Messrs Harrison, Cann & Co., and remained in their possession down to 1875. During Harrison's time as the local phrase puts it, the only incidents of note were the underground fire, caused by a boiler fire of a large pump, fixed in the dip workings, to cope with an extraordinary amount of water. The fire was eventually walled off, and only caused a short stoppage. The other incident caused a stoppage of much longer duration, and was the result of the breakdown of the large pumping set, causing the colliery to be laid in for a good many months, and necessitated the male population to find work elsewhere.

In 1875, Harrison disposed of the interest in the harbour to Mr H. Andrews the then owner of Broomhill Colliery, and Radcliffe again changed hands, passing to Messrs. Haggie, Smith & Co.

In 1892, it was found necessary to abandon the old colliery owing to a fault throwing down the coal seams to the south, and new shafts were sunk about a mile to the southeast of the old colliery. Eight years later Newborough, the name given to the new colliery was incorporated in the new company formed under the registered title of Broomhill Collieries Limited, which included both collieries, harbour, ships, etc.

Considerable developments have been carried out under the new Company who also acquired the land Royalties and other manorial privileges which originally belonged to the ancient line of Radcliffes.

A new railway line connects Broomhill Colliery with the old Radcliffe Colliery wagon-way to Amble, thus completing an independent connection with the harbour. Considerable extensions have also been carried out in the underground workings, and the Royalties previously belonging to Broomhill on the western boundary are now worked from Newborough Colliery, and the output has steadily increased to over 1200 tons daily.

The following estimate of one year's working of Radcliffe Colliery in the year 1840, taken from the Company's books, in comparison with the present day cost of working price of coal, etc., will prove interesting reading.

Estimate of the annual expenses of working and putting on board ship 79,500 tons of best coal.

To produce 79,500 tons best coal or 30,000 chaldrons of coal will require 20,000 scores of 6 tons each, or 120,000 tons to be wrought.

ESTIMATED UNDERGROUND CHARGES ON THIS QUANTITY

	£	s.	d.
20,000 hewing at 6s. including narrow and double working and wet ...	6000	0	0
2000 putting at 1s. 6d. including furtherance and helping up	150	0	0

TRAP DOOR KEEPING

	£	s.	d.
12 boys, 270 days=3240 days at 10d. ...	135	0	0

DRIVING

	£	s.	d.
16 boys, 270 days=4320 days at 1s. 3d. per day	270	0	0
2 water leaders and jobbing men, 540 days at 2s.	54	0	0
2 wood leaders, 540 days at 1s. 6d. ...	40	10	0
4 platelayers, rolley, 1080 days at 2s. 10d.	153	0	0
2 overmen, 52 weeks at 24s.	124	16	0
2 onsetters, 540 days at 3s. 6d.	94	10	0

	£	s.	d.
4 deputy overmen, 52 weeks each at 21s.	218	8	0
6 wastemen and shifters, ridding falls, pumping water, etc., 1620 days at 3s.	243	0	0
1 underground horsekeeper, 52 weeks at 16s.	41	12	0
2 furnacemen, each 52 weeks at 16s. ...	83	4	0
Keep of 10 underground horses at £52, 10s.	525	0	0

Bank Charges

4 bankmen including waiting on	220	0	0
1 heapkeeper, 52 weeks at 18s.	46	16	0
8 waiters, each 270 days=2160 days at 10d.	90	0	0
4 wagonmen, 52 weeks at 38s.	98	6	0
4 screenmen, each 270 days=1080 at 3s.	162	0	0
Filling coals, 15,000 chlds. at 3d.	187	10	0

Engines and Machines

2 plugmen, each 52 weeks at 23s. 4d. ...	121	6	8
4 firemen, each 52 weeks at 17s.	176	16	0
2 changers and grathers, each 52 weeks at 21s.	109	4	0
3 brakesmen at machines with spare ditto for other work, 52 weeks at 38s. ...	98	6	0
3 firemen at machines, each 52 weeks at 16s.	134	16	0

Upperground Horses

	£	s.	d.
Wagons, 4, Cart and Jack, 6, Saddle, 1, Crab, 1, total, 12 at £50	600	0	0
Salaries including fitting	1000	0	0
Surgery	50	0	0

Colliery Rent

	£	s.	d.
Best coal, 1636 tons at 18s. = £1472 8 0 } Small coal, 218 tons at 9s. = £98 2 0 }	1570	10	0
Way leave rent	450	0	0
Damage of ground, trespass, etc.	30	0	0
8 blacksmiths, each 312 days = 2496 days at 3s.	374	8	0
6 carpenters and sawyers, 52 weeks each at 18s.	280	16	0
4 masons, 52 weeks each at 18s.	187	4	0
3 masons' labourers, 52 weeks each at 15s.	117	0	0
Tradesmen's bills, timber, iron, ropes, etc.	3000	0	0
Unforeseen incidents	288	4	0

TOGSTON

This small hamlet, known in ye olden times by the various names of Doxton, Toggesdon, etc., is situated on the highway a mile south-west of Amble.

Almost every vestige of a village has been wiped out with the large block of wooden houses which fell into decay some time ago.

Togston Hall, now the property of the Dand family, the Mansion House of the Smith estates, and two or three houses, constitute all that remains of the ancient hamlet. Unlike the two neighbouring villages, Amble and Warkworth, which were Church lands, Togston seems to have payed fealty to the Crown, and to the earlier Lords of Warkworth. In the twelfth century three-fourths of the land in the Manor of Toggesdon was held by Ralph Fitz Main, the King's forester in Northumberland, as sergeant of the King.

From time to time different parts of the

lands of Togston were held as knight's services. Later, we find some famous Northumbrian families holding land in the "vill of Toggesdon," viz. the Carnaby's, Grey's, Fenwick's, Haggerston's, Radcliffe's, etc. Ultimately the Haggerston lands, i.e. Togston Barns, were conveyed to William Smith in 1812, this family having previously acquired parcels of land in the township. The Radcliffe's portion, Togston Moor House (now Low Hall) passed to the descendants of the Radcliffe's—Lady Newborough, with the other portions of land in Amble, Warkworth, and Hauxley, confiscated in 1715, and is now the property of the Broomhill Collieries Limited. The remaining portion came into the possession of Edward Cook, and passed with his only daughter and heiress to Isaac Cookson, who sold it to James Dand of Hauxley in 1832, and is still retained in that family.

From very early in the last century, mining operations have been carried on in this township of Togston, and coals carted from Togston were shipped at Amble in 1826, ten years before the Warkworth Harbour Act was obtained. The colliery from which this coal was obtained was known as South

Togston, situated close by the Amble Branch Railway, and is now part of Broomhill Colliery. Another shaft was near the cottages at the turn of the road to Amble. There are quite a number of old shafts scattered over other parts of the township, principally on the Dand estate.

Amongst the many ventures is what is known as " Gibbon's Seam," worked on either side of the highway near the Togston Hollow. This is the same seam that was worked so extensively round Amble, on the north of the great upcast fault.

Another mining venture is the one known as Mole's Pit, in the green field near the top of the bank on the Amble road, and a pool of water still marks the spot. The shaft of this pit was sunk on the side of the Hauxley Fault, to what is known as the " Princess Seam " and a rather peculiar history hangs round the old shaft. The story goes that when Mr Dand purchased the Togston estate, he did not acquire the mineral rights. He afterwards found that the seam was being worked dangerously near his residence, and he acquired the Royalty and gave notice to cease mining operations. To this the mine-owner refused to consent, and a battle of cross-purposes commenced. In the first place Mr Dand had the machinery dismantled, but the intrepid miner was not to be outdone and he descended the shaft under cover of darkness, drew out the timber supports round the shaft bottom, and closed the entrance to the workings. When the miners arrived next morning they found the machinery dismantled and the mine closed.

Sixty years later the writer holed into these workings and after the water and carbonic acid gas were cleared the working places were found with the miners' tools, etc., just as they had left them, with the exception that the iron was very much oxidised. The system of mining was to remove two feet of under clay and "nick" both sides of a place nine feet wide, leaving two yards of solid coal between the places for support.

Several years later Cowan's commenced the Plantation Pit, about a hundred yards west, but stopped midway in an attempt to win the main seam. He then made another venture a little further west and struck the main seam at ten fathoms. This turned out a good speculation, and for many years did an exceptionally large landsale trade. Stories are told of carts from long distances having to wait here days together to get a load of coal. The coal was of an exceptionally good quality; a thick seam situated between a risefault on either side, with the outcrop to the west, which rather limited the coal-producing area.

Messrs Pyman, Bell & Co. succeeded Cowan's and continued sinking the Plantation Pit down to the main seam. This, however, turned out a failure after a large sum of money had been spent on the venture.

The next attempt was the Gin Pit in the westfield, a little south of Cowan's pit, but a rise trouble considerably changed the quality and thickness of the seam. Another pit was sunk near the footpath to Amble, but was much affected with "troubles" and old workings, and had only a short existence as a colliery.

The recent undertaking, the pit near the railway and at the boundary of the Royalty, was the most extensive of all—sunk to the Radcliffe bed, with all the seams on in good condition. A siding was connected with the railway, and housing accommodation for a large number of workmen was provided at Amble, together with all the requirements of an up-to-date colliery. But the same dogged

ill-luck which characterised all previous
Togston mining enterprises ended in this
case with a partial collapse of the shaft, and
Togston has, in all probability, seen the last
of many unsuccessful mining ventures.

BROOMHILL

THE neighbouring colliery village is situated in the township of Chevington, east, two miles distant from Amble, and was originally part of the old extensive Parish of Warkworth. At the present time Broomhill, together with several other small villages and hamlets, comprise the Parish of Chevington.

The extensive lands and other manorial privileges of the township have from time to time been held by the Morwicks, Widdringtons, etc., but are now almost the exclusive possessions of Earl Grey of Howick.

Broomhill is sometimes described as Amble's " main artery "; and it is certain that the present-day importance of the small port is in a large measure due to the great development of Broomhill Colliery. The colliery village is comparatively recent, and, generally speaking, the housing accommodation is of the improved type, and the back-to-back fever-producing slums once so prevalent in the North of England, have never been in evidence here.

The original village is in two parts; one situated near the colliery proper, close by the highway, with well-kept gardens in front, the other is half a mile distant to the south on the same highway, and in both cases the sanitary conditions have always been of the very much improved colliery village type.

In recent years there has been considerable development in the building line. This commenced in 1886 in the construction of a new village in the township of Togston which eventually took the name of Togston Terrace. The new village is almost entirely owned by miners employed at the colliery. Besides, the new village has two public places of worship, a very fine Workmen's Social Club, and other places of business.

At a still more recent date another prosperous village has sprung up, viz. the Red Row, about two miles distant from the colliery. Twenty-five years ago where there was only a blacksmith's shop and house there is now a large village, and the population numbers nearly one thousand.

There are up-to-date shops, two places of

worship, viz. the Wesleyan Methodists and English Presbyterian Chapels, a splendid new Council School, and a large Workmen's Social Club. Close by is the first Trust public-house, a movement which has for its object, the turning of profit from "drink" (after paying interest on capital expenditure) to assist the rates. The object so far has not been a complete success.

Speculators in the building line have taken the advantage of cheap building land on either side of the highway and have almost joined up the villages. On this line also stands the Church of England, the Board Schools, the Co-operative Society, and the Wesleyan Chapel, and are the most conspicuous features of a long straggling "street."

Broomhill has been connected with mining from time immemorial, and an old resident, Mr C. Purvis, tells of his ancestors being connected with mining operations in the district for the past two hundred years. This early mining is accounted for by the outcrop of the Northumberland main seam, in good condition half a mile to the west, and to-day the coal which attracted the pioneers in mining can be seen in a roadside quarry

almost on the surface. All along this outcropping line are mounds which mark the
early operations, and the almost regular
intervening spaces of the various shafts go to
prove that sinking and drifting was even at
this early period a comparatively easy task.
From this experience of simply digging coals
near the surface it seems to have been per-
severed with, and old shafts can be traced
eastwards to the site of the now famous
Broomhill Colliery sunk to a depth of forty-
five fathoms.

The past history of this mining village as
regards its early industries, etc., is meagre
and unimportant, but its recent mining history
marks an epoch in an advanced, progressive
age. In the latter part of the past century
Broomhill Colliery had for many years the
record of drawing more coals from one shaft
in a working day than any other colliery in
the world. Besides, for about a quarter of
a century the " pit " was never idle for want
of trade, and another noteworthy incident
was that only on very rare occasions a
stranger was taken on at the colliery, the
young putter-hewers keeping up the supply.

This remarkable progress was entirely
due to the great enterprising business

capacity of Mr Hugh Andrews who became a partner in the Company in 1871.

A few years later the services of J. H. Merivale, Esq., Professor of Mining at Durham College of Science, was secured, and from a daily output of 1000 tons it rose to 2000 tons.

The Harbour Debentures Bonds were also secured by the Company and the hitherto humdrum village of Amble was transformed into an active seaport town.

In the year 1900, Mr Andrews severed his connection with Broomhill, which, together with Radcliffe Colliery, was purchased by a new Company, and are now known under the title of "the Broomhill Collieries Limited."

WARKWORTH VILLAGE.

[*Photo by W. G. Chambers.*

WARKWORTH CASTLE.

[*Photo by W. G. Chambers.*

CHEVINGTON DRIFT

THIS very modern colliery village had its origin in the development of the Broomhill Collieries Limited, as recent as 1900. As the workings of the Broomhill Colliery extended in a south-easterly direction, to relieve the drag on ventilation, etc., a day drift was constructed in the year 1888, with the opening near East Chevington Farm. At first only a few houses were built, but when the present Company took over the colliery it was then contemplated to double the output. Extensive boring operations were carried out, and housing accommodation was provided for the proposed development of a new and extensive coal area. The place chosen for the new colliery community cannot be described as a pleasing outlook, on the contrary it is bleak and monotonous in the extreme. Not a scrap of woodland anywhere, only a stretch of low-lying land for miles around. The close proximity to the sea is a redeeming feature, as it forms the background on the east to a broad expanse of monotonous landscape. Nor has the laying-out of the new town added to its attractiveness, for it consists of two long rows of cottages nearly a mile in length with one opening about midway. Otherwise the conditions are fairly good as far as sanitary conditions, etc., are concerned in a colliery village. There are very few institutions in the new community, and these comprise a Mechanics Institute, a small Primitive Methodist Chapel and a branch Co-operative Store.

Quite recently Earl Grey very magnanimously gave a piece of land at the west end of the village to build Aged Miners' Homes. The style of architecture of the buildings is an improvement on the surrounding houses, and the pretty garden patch in front gives the aged veterans' residences quite a pleasant appearance.

The population is estimated to be over a thousand.

WARKWORTH

THIS little volume would not be complete without some brief allusion to the pretty and essentially historic hamlet.

The history of Amble is dull, meagre, and unromantic, with scarcely a single incident outside the " humdrum drudgery " of every-day life, while on the other hand Warkworth finds an interesting place in history from Bede's Chronicles until comparatively recent times. Besides, the connection with the dawn of Christianity, the military fame of Hotspur, the great genius of Shakespeare and the halo of romance which hangs round its Hermitage have all added a peculiar charm to this old-time village.

Of its picturesque surroundings, its beautiful sylvan scenery, folded in the embrace of the king of Northumbrian streams, it is unnecessary to dilate, except to mention that the " sleepy Hollow " lays a strong claim to the disputed title of " Queen of Northumbrian Villages."

Warkworth claims to have been originally a Saxon village where the early settlers built a stockaded town, having landed in the estuary of the Coquet with their flat-bottomed boats. Even to-day there are traces of the inner town and the garden-patch with the outlands lying beyond, mainly to the south and west, which, at a later date, became the park and demesne lands of the lordly Norman.

That the inhabitants early embraced Christianity there is little doubt, for we find that in 737, Wercewood was included in the five villages conferred on the monastery of Lindisfarne by the Saxon King Ceolwoulph, where he retired later to lead the saintly life and

> " For cowl and beads laid down
> The Saxon battle axe and crown."

To Ceolwoulph the little hamlet owes its place in history, as he is said to have built a little wooden church to exert civilising influence on the rude Saxons. Later, Warkworth felt the full force of the ruthless Dane, and amongst other ravages in Northumberland laid the village waste.

It is to the Normans we turn for the real, interesting period of the little hamlet. Warkworth was included amongst other extensive grants of land to the powerful Mowbray by William the Conqueror. It is really with a successive grant by Henry II. to Roger Fitz Richard, who, if he did not raise the first building, was the first to give to Warkworth a real Castle, around which is woven a wealth of military renown of which the villagers are justly proud.

The Claverings having died out in the heir male line, the Barony of Warkworth was conferred on the Earls of Northumberland by Edward III. From this time onward, through the troublesome times of the Wars of the Roses, Warkworth carried the title of being the great storm centre of a stormy time.

It was here the fiery Hotspur organised plots against his Sovereign Lord, and it was from Warkworth he often hied to meet in mortal strife the gallant Douglas, his brave but relentless foe on many a bloody field. The early death of Hotspur on the plain of Shrewsbury did not end the trouble at Warkworth, for a little later Henry IV. marched an army of 37,000 men against Warkworth

L

and its rebellious Earl. Against the walls of Warkworth was brought into use almost the first cannon in England. At the seventh round we are told the Castle capitulated, and the days of the feudal stronghold were over.

In the Wars of the Roses Warkworth played some little part, as the second and third earls died for the Red Rose.

On more than one occasion Warkworth suffered severely at the hands of the Scots. William the Lion, King of Scotland in 1137, descended on Warkworth, captured the Castle, threw down its earthen walls, and retired without striking a blow. A year later one of the Lion King's generals, Duncan, Earl of Fife, swooped down on Warkworth, burnt the town, and slew the inhabitants. Not even those who took shelter in the sacred edifice were spared, and men, women, and children were put to death, according to some authorities to the number of three hundred. Again in 1341, the Scots, previous to the relief of Wark, sacked and burnt the town of Warkworth. In 1428, in one of the Douglas raids on Northumberland, Warkworth was again destroyed.

The Castle, still a grim sentinel of a

stormy past, so aptly described by Shakespeare in Henry IV. as

> " That worm-eaten hold of rugged stone
>   Where old Northumberland lies crafty sick."

is the very acme of a border stronghold.

Its fighting towers, its massive walls, its capacity for storing supplies, and, above all, its elevated position made it, as history tells us, a safe refuge on many a memorable occasion against powerful odds.

Inside the courtyard, the great rendezvous of holiday crowds, there is ample scope for a world of thought, and here the student of history, architecture, and antiquarian lore can alike revel in the extremely interesting surroundings.

The village is now fast losing its old-world aspect. The thatched roof has entirely disappeared, and there is only a semblance of the red pan tile roof remaining to give a little tone to the sleepy hollow. The cobble stones by the side of the highway remain only in some instances where it suits the taste of the owner, and in recent renovations in a good many cases the cobbles give place to the more modern cement.

It is certainly not a desirable movement to

destroy these last traces of a bygone age, as up-to-date modern town conditions will ultimately rob the old-world hamlet of its greatest charm. There are only a few houses where the inscriptions take us back to the eighteenth century, and their very quaintness reflects refreshing glimpses of " ye olden times."

The church alone remains intact, close by the murmuring Coquet to remind us of a remote past, for we are told, on reliable authority, that the present church is built on the site, and includes some parts of the pre-Conquest Saxon building. This fine old Norman structure seems to have been saved from the vandal restoration craze of the early part of the last century, so common in the north, and the nave still retains, in the main, its original style, varying from the Norman architecture of 1130, to the transitional period. The aisle is Early English, and affords a good opportunity to even the amateur archæologist to contrast the different styles of architecture, viz. the severe horse-shoe Norman arch, and the gracefully pointed arch of the Early English period.

There is also evidence that the sacred building has passed through troublesome days, and there are traces of the ravages of Border Wars still visible. Besides, there is the memory of the massacre within the sacred precincts by the dastardly cruel Scot, and this is part of the grim annals of Warkworth Church. In later days the church again figures in the rebellion of 1715, as a small band of followers of the Pretender spent the Sunday in Warkworth, and their chaplain, the Rev. Buxton, took possession of the pulpit, and prayed for his King, James III.

The venerable pile is surrounded by an equally venerable God's acre long since filled up with the bones of the worthies of the little hamlet for long past ages.

THE BRIDGE

Near by the old church is the fourteenth-century bridge of two arches, with a ruined gateway tower at the south end. Its narrow roadway and its triangular refuge-places at the crown is a little out of date for the traffic of the twentieth century. It is ill-suited indeed for the modern motor-car or cycle, besides the almost continuous cab traffic to and from the railway station. Yet in spite of the enormous amount of inconvenience the old-world bridge entails to the hurry-scurry be-quick movements of the present time, there are not a few who would regret any attempt to modernise this old link with the past.

Strength seems to have been the chief consideration of the original builders, and the floods of four centuries have failed to make any impression on its well-devised piers. A way round the gateway tower has in recent years considerably relieved the congested traffic, besides allowing large caravans to pass over the bridge, which in former times were unable to do so, on account of the low archway.

Down to comparatively recent years the porters' room in the old gateway tower was used as a gaol, or lock-up for village brawlers and other disturbers of the public peace.

On a piece of waste land by the river-side stands the old school-house granted to the village by Mr G. Lawson of Gloster Hill. For many years this building not only fulfilled the educational needs but was also used as the public meeting-place. The question now arises, the old legacy is out of date and what shall be done with the " aud skeul " is puzzling the village worthies who now control the affairs of the burgesses.

" Round by Ember " is a familiar phrase, which means the footpath round the eastern side of the village, probably the eastern boundary of the primitive stockaded Saxon town. Here also are the villagers' gardens, which have made Warkworth famous in the horticultural world.

The Butts is the portion of the village on the low-lying flats by the river-side on the east of the ancient village, and appears to be of recent date, in fact it may be readily assumed that this part of Warkworth has been reclaimed from the old river-bed.

The New Town is a stretch of land lying between the village and the sea, comprising about fifty acres. The eastern extremity was the original river-mouth, and a fishing village is supposed to have existed here. The principal portion of the land is the burgesses' half-acres, the other half is rented from the Duke of Northumberland.

There are now remaining seventy-seven burgesses who own houses and plots of freehold land in the village, at the New Town, Heather Leazes, and the common land on Warkworth Moor. After the Inclosures Act, certain burgesses sold their respective portions of common land, given by Sir Hugh-de-Morwick to the town of Warkworth in 1200, to the Duke of Northumberland, who is Lord of the Manor, and owns most of the land in the district.

In former times there were three fairs held during the year. One on the Thursday before the Feast of Saint George's Day in the month of April, one on the Thursday before the Feast of Saint Lawrence, to whom the old church is dedicated, in the month of

August, and the other on the Thursday before Martinmas. in November. The latter until recently was recognised in a way, but is now discontinued, and not even the pig-cart is in evidence to make the old fair a sort of farce. The holding of " the Court Leet " and other remnants of feudal times are still commemorated in order to retain the slender link that connects the village rule of the remote past with the present.

THE HERMITAGE

There are few more enchanting and romantic spots than Warkworth Hermitage.

To reach the anchorite's cell, a boat is provided by the Duke of Northumberland, the owner, and visitors are taken up the river by the custodian of the Castle from a point near the old stronghold.

This trip on the silvery Coquet, with the reflection of the rugged fortress in the water, the thickly wooded banks, and the ever frolicking fish, to dwellers under smoke-laden skies must be a real feast of nature.

The Hermitage can also be reached by the footpath known as the Mill Walk, which skirts the Castle's grim walls by the river-side, emerging half a mile farther on to a beautiful forest glade. Giant trees, silent sentinels of a forgotten past, with ever-varying hues, beautiful and luxuriant under-growth, wild flowers in great profusion, together with a wealth of wild ferns and mosses all contribute to lend a charm to this pretty spot. Here in this wonderland of flowers and foliage, with the silvery Coquet forming a semicircle round a grassy mound on the opposite bank of the river, is the little Hermitage built in a rock so graphically described in Spencer's stanza:

> " A little lowly Hermitage it was
>   Down in a dale hard by a forest side.
>   Far from resort of people that did pass
>   In travel to and fro a little wide.
>   There was a holy chapel edified,
>   Wherein the hermit duly wont to say
>   His holy things each morn and eventide.
>   Thereby a crystal stream did gently play,
>   Which from a sacred fountain welled away."

In busy holiday times, visitors are ferried across the river to a landing-place a little below the Hermitage, and a short walk under a canopy, formed by the overhanging branches reaching to the water edge, considerably enhances the charming solitude of the surroundings and brings the visitor to the hermit's abode in days of old. The first object that meets the eye is a building that formed the dwelling-place of the recluse, and from evident traces of comfortable conditions you are inclined to come to the conclusion that

the hermits of Warkworth (at least the latter-
day occupants) were not quite so frugal in
their habits as the holy hermit of the lonely
Farnes or the hermit of Coquet Island. The
spacious fire-place, the traces of a large oven
and other signs are evident that the later
occupants of the cell knew something of the
culinary art.

All traces of the well-stocked orchard and
large garden mentioned in old documents are
now lost. The garden is supposed to have
been on the flat near the domicile by the
river-side, the orchard on the top of the high
bank, and was reached by a flight of crude
steps cut through the cliff, which are still in
evidence.

It is to the rock-hewn chapel, however, that
visitors naturally turn their close attention,
which is approached by steps from the base
of the domestic building to a higher face of
the cliff. Here in every detail, in spite of the
wasting ravages of time and the barbarous
vandalism of recent times, is still a perfect
miniature pre-Reformation Church. In the
entrance porch there are the usual side seats
of rough-hewn rock and over the entrance
there is still the faint outline of the Cruci-
fixion, with the dying Saviour extended on

THE BRIDGE, WARKWORTH.

[*Photo by W. G. Chambers.*]

HERMITAGE, WARKWORTH.

[*Photo by W. G. Chambers.*

the Cross, and on either side is the Blessed Virgin and Saint John. Immediately over this door, on the inner side, was the plaintive cry of the psalmist inscribed in Latin, " My tears have been my bread both day and night."

The chapel is eighteen feet long by seven feet wide, of most exquisite workmanship—the central bosses, the diagonal ribs and mouldings, hewn out of the solid rock, are intensely descriptive of fourteenth-century architecture. The altar remains intact, and is unique, being the only altar that escaped effacement or destruction in Northumberland during the Reformation Period. The great attraction of the present-day visitors is the group of figures in the recess, which include the recumbent figure of a female, over which the kneeling figure of a man weeps in seeming contemplation. There is also the figure of an angel near the shoulder, and at the feet the head of an ox. Over this group the sentimental visitor ponders long in contemplation of Dr Percy's romantic and pathetic tragedy in the remote Cheviot glen " far from the abode of men."

On the north side of the outer chapel is a crude, cave-shaped room, but on closer examination it proves to be another chapel, considered to be much more ancient than the outer one.

Between the outer and inner chapels, near the altar of both there is a very fine tracery window, besides other openings of a less artistic design.   Over the entrance door to this chapel from the outer building is still the traces of the emblem of the Passion, i.e. the Cross, the Crown, and Spear, but the Latin inscription which accompanied it, " They gave me gall for my meat and in my thirst they gave me vinegar to drink," has now entirely disappeared.   This part is open at the west end and the altar stone is much damaged, said to be the work of treasure seekers, owing to there being a hollow sound in the rock behind the altar, caused by a split in the cliff.

There are the remains of another room, supposed to have been a dormitory, which is without windows and opens into the principal chapel.   Other portions supposed to have been a gallery have been demolished by a fall of rock, leaving only the ledge.

The earliest authentic history in connection with the Hermitage is where it is described as the Chapel of the Holy Trinity in Sunderland Park, this being the name of my Lord Warkworth's deer forest. The chaplain in 1487 was Thomas Barker, subsequently followed by John Green and Edward Sligg, the latter being appointed in 1515.

The last beneficiary, Sir George Lancaster, a friend of the Earl of Northumberland, was appointed in 1531, and his revenues were liberal, viz. " a yearly stipend of twenty marks, twelve kye and a bull, with calves sucking, two horses, twenty loads of firewood, and every Sunday a draught of ' fysshe.' "

The little Chapel of the Trinity doubtless disappeared at the Reformation, although the altar was not overthrown, at least for the practice of the old religion.

The origin of the Hermitage is evolved out of a good deal of obscurity, and is ascribed to the first Earl of Northumberland and the monks of Alnwick Abbey, but most authorities consider it to have been a hermit's cell at a much earlier date. The figures in the recess, all capable judges essentially agree, in spite of the popular opinion, represent the Nativity, viz. the Blessed Virgin and Holy Child, the Shepherd and the ox, all emblematical of the Cave at Bethlehem. But lest too close a scrutiny of history might destroy

the weird charm which Dr Percy has woven
round the hermit of Warkworth it might be
well to defer any further investigation, and
refer lovers of romance to Dr Percy's version
" The Hermit's Tale," that weird, fascinating, distressful tragedy in the Cheviot glen,
of which the following is a summary.

THE HERMIT OF WARKWORTH

In this charming ballad, fragments of border history, legendary lore, and tragedy are beautifully blended, and around the luckless hermit is woven a tragic tale of woe.

After the death of Hotspur at the Battle of Shrewsbury the aged Earl of Northumberland fled to Scotland, taking with him the only son of the fiery Hotspur. Imbued with the spirit of his father the young hope of Northumberland prevailed upon his grandsire to allow him to visit his native land disguised as a hunter. Having obtained service in the house of the Earl of Westmorland he won favour with the Baron's daughter, by chivalrously rescuing her from a band of Border troopers. After learning the true name and birth of her rescuer the daughter of the powerful noble vowed to wed the banished scion of the Percy's. There being only a remote chance of the princely mother, sister of Henry Bollingbroke, ever looking kindly

on the union with the exiled son of the
rebellious Hotspur, the lovers decided to
elope, and fled to Scotland.   Fearing they
were pursued they took shelter in the woods
near the hermit's cell where the holy man
found the runaway pair, and hospitably extended to them both shelter and food.   To
the recluse they told their tale, disclosing the
fact that the youth was the hope of the Percy
line, the son of the lonely hermit's dearest
friend, he in turn unfolding his own pathetic
life story.

Isabel Widdrington the fair daughter of
the Lord of that ilk had many suitors, but
Bertram the neighbouring Baron of Bothal
was the most favoured.   In the days of
ancient chivalry the axiom that " none but
the brave deserve the fair " was observed, and
the maiden demanded some tangible proof
that the gallant knight was worthy of her love.
Accordingly she sent him a beautiful casque
and consented to be his bride when this had
been severely tried in mortal combat.

The opportunity for such a test in these
stormy days was of daily occurrence, and the
bold Percy led an incursion to the Border
side.   In a tilt with the implacable Scots,
Bertram's casque, his lady's gift, was put to

a severe test, and after a display of extraordinary valour the brave Baron was stricken
down and the precious helmet cleft in twain.
Stricken with remorse Isabel wept for her
wounded lover's fate and at once set out for
Wark, where the fallen knight lay sick unto
death, to nurse him back to health.   On her
way she was accosted by a disappointed
suitor who slew her guards and carried her off
to his castle in a remote Cheviot glen.

In due course Bertram recovered from his
wounds and hastened to Widdrington to claim
his well-earned love.   To his dismay the aged
nurse of fair Isabel told of how the maiden,
sad at heart, had set out long before to attend
his sick-bed.   To find his lost love Bertram
and a younger brother swore a solemn com-
pact to scour the country round and never
cease until they had found his lady fair, dead
or alive.

Disguised as a minstrel the lover knight,
wandering by the Border side, was accosted
by an aged palmer that his mien ill became
a minstrel.   This exchange of courtesies led
to the unfolding of his task, and from the
aged man he got tidings of his missing love.
The tidings proved true, and he eventually
found her safely guarded in a strong fortress.

The manner by which he could effect an escape
was absorbing his attention when he found
to his dismay that another more fortunate
youth had effected her rescue and was carrying her off before his eyes.   Blinded by fury
he followed the flying pair and demanded
possession of the fair prisoner.   The rescuer,
who happened to be his more resourceful
brother, maddened at the thought of having
to give up his precious charge to her erstwhile
captors, rushed on the challenger,

"But Bertram's stronger hand prevailed and laid the
     stranger low,"

and Isabel recognising her lover's voice
rushed between the combatants and received
a fatal wound.

After realising that in his blind rage he
had unwittingly killed his own brother and
accidentally slain his lost love, he was over-
whelmed with remorse, and it was only by
force that he was restrained from taking his
life, by a crowd from the Castle in hot pursuit
of the recently escaped precious charge.   For
long Bertram's reason battled with despair

"Till time and books and holy men, had better
     counsels taught."

Ultimately he gave his lands to feed the

poor, vowed to spend his remaining days in penance and prayer in an anchorite cell, and retired from the world to the little Hermitage in a secluded glen near his erstwhile comrade in arms, the impetuous knight of the Hot Spur.

WARKWORTH MILL

Close by the Hermitage a little higher up the river is Warkworth Mill—"My Lord's Mill" so frequently mentioned in the Amble accounts during the priory rule. An old record states that "my Lord had two milns in Sunderland Park and the tennents in the townships of Amble, Hauxley, Buston, Acklington, Spittle and Brotherwick, were constrained to have their corn ground at the Parish Mill at a certain moulture, i.e. one-fourteenth."

That the "Lord" took care of this protected privilege is proved by the instance of the monks' windmill on Coquet Island. The holy man having invented and constructed a windmill to grind his corn, and lest this mill might come into competition with his mill, the then Lord Roger Fitz Roger at the head of a force of armed men landed on the island and threw down the hermit's mill. There can be little doubt that this mill was the

principal mill of the district for centuries. At
the beginning of the last century a very
extensive business in grinding was carried on,
giving employment to a lot of people. In
1860, it was partially destroyed by fire.

The advent of steam and railways gave the
death-blow to the rural mill, Warkworth Mill
being no exception, and the business on a
more extensive system was transferred to
Newcastle. The old mill was put to a new
use, viz. to capture salmon in the old mill-
race styled the " Locks," and it was here, in
1865, that the determined attempt was made
to exterminate the bull-trout by wholesale
slaughter. Larger catches of salmon became
the rule by this process, and the riparian
owners in the upper reaches of the river raised
a great cry against the Locks, which were
abolished, and net fishing in the tidal waters
again established.

The dam is all that now remains to prove
the existence of the parish mill in days gone
by, and a pretty cottage and garden marks
the spot of my Lord's mill of long ago.

GEOLOGY

THE chief object in introducing a geological chapter into this volume is to induce at least young readers to take an interest in this subject. It is strange, but nevertheless true, that there are very few in Amble and district that take an interest in this wonderful science, in spite of the fact that the daily occupation of a mining population gives such admirable facilities to become acquainted with geology.

There will be no attempt to dilate on the advanced stages of this wonderful science, but rather an attempt to induce ordinary individuals to take an interest in geology in their walks abroad, when they will never fail to meet with indisputable ocular demonstrations of the building up of the earth's crust, otherwise known as the science of geology.

To the amateur geologist the building up of the solid earth is indescribably interesting, and to the learned expert the composition of the earth is an open book gathered from close

184

observations in deep gorges, sea cliffs, quarries, coal mines, etc.

As it is my purpose to deal only with the chief interesting geological features of the immediate neighbourhood which are exposed principally on the coast-line, the valley of the Coquet, etc., it will only be necessary to refer briefly to the older formations—igneous rocks, of which we have no trace in the locality, except in the case of dykes, whin cells, etc.

IGNEOUS ROCKS

The igneous rocks take us back to the formation of the earth's crust. As the name implies, these rocks are the result of fire, the cooling down of the molten condition which formed the crust of the solid earth.

Although igneous rocks are the original substance, granite and basalt rocks are found at various ages of the earth, both as eruptive rocks from volcanic action, and as intrusive rocks where the molten fluid was forced into cavities, displacing softer substances, and does not reach the surface except by the more recent folding of the earth's crust, or by denudation.

Granite is composed of quartz, felspar, horneblende, and mica, and these minerals in various quantities are found to comprise the chief structure of the igneous formation.

The Cheviots are a good instance of volcanic action, and well repay a visit from the amateur geologist.

Of intrusive rocks some remarkable instances are on view on the shore near Craster, and notable instances of whin cells are to be seen on the coast-line from Boulmer to Berwick. Whin dykes also belong to the igneous eruptic rocks, and one of the most interesting geological features of the district is the famous Acklington Dyke, said to extend from sea to sea, viz. from Bondicar near Radcliffe in a practically straight line west, right through the Cheviot Range and south of Scotland to the Irish Sea. A peculiar feature of the dyke is that it varies in width and its distance from the surface, in its course. For instance, at Radcliffe there is no indication near the surface, but when cut through in the mine it was found to be two feet thick, while a mile farther west at Broomhill, it is twice cut through in the Togston district and is ten yards across. East of Acklington it is not exposed to the surface, but to the west it is found very frequently exposed until it passes beneath the Framlington Hills, appearing again at Cartington, and wherever exposed it is quarried for road metal right along its course to the Cheviots.

ARCHEAN SYSTEM.—The first of the sedimentary rocks is known as the Archean

System, built up of decomposed fragments of igneous rocks. It is chiefly interesting as having contained, according to some geologists, Eozoon or dawn of life in the shape of coral zoophytes. It is also said to contain graphite composed mainly of carbon—the origin of the vegetable world, but on these points scientists are not agreed. These rocks are found in the north-west of Scotland and in Pembrokeshire.

THE CAMBRIAN SYSTEM.—Next is the Cambrian System which shows distinct fossils of animal and vegetable life. These rocks are highly developed in North Wales.

THE SILURIAN SYSTEM.—Overlying the Cambrian, is the Silurian System with still more signs of life, and can be seen a little north of Berwick.

THE DEVONIAN SYSTEM.—Next in order is the Devonian or Old Red Sandstone, distinctly different from the previous systems. These rocks are considerably more interesting locally, as traces of red sandstone can be found round the base of the Cheviots, and undoubtedly formed the sea bottom out of which the active volcano belched forth fire and fumes in building up the Cheviot Range.

CARBONIFEROUS SYSTEM.—It is with the

Carboniferous System that real interest in geology to the ordinary man begins. The Mountain Limestone forms the base of this system, and these rocks are especially interesting in the North of England.

After the formation of the red sandstone there was quite a new order of things. Up to this time life on earth was very limited, but a great change took place, and, in a warm sea, myriads of the lower forms of shell-fish came into existence, and eventually built up the base of the Carboniferous System, known as the Mountain Limestone in the Midlands, and as the Bernician in the North of England.

For untold ages these coral reefs went on forming from the dead bodies of the various shell-fish, and they attain their greatest thickness in Derbyshire and Somersetshire, but gradually thin away to the North of England, which appears to have been the shore of that ancient sea.

To the south, the sea seems to have been open, and far removed from the shore, consequently affording abundant facilities for the various forms of shell-fish which swarmed its waters, the residue of which formed these now exposed mountains of limestone in the vicinity of Buxton and Matlock, the Cheddar Cliffs and the dales of North Yorkshire.

Passing northwards, the conditions were different, and as the sea became shallower it got stilted, and layers of sandstone, shale, and coal are intermixed. These are known as Yoredale rocks in Yorkshire and gradually get thicker, with a consequent thinning of the limestone from high hills to mere panels. As it extended still farther northward, mud and fine sand completely stilted up the sea to such an extent that the shell-forming limestone disappears as a fundamental base to the Carboniferous System.

There are few places where such facilities are offered to observe this wonderful structure, than in our own county.

The northern outcrop, the Felltop Limestone, appears on the south-west border of Northumberland, passes west through Cumberland and Westmorland, while its eastern outcrop passes in a triangular line across Northumberland to a point a little north of Alnmouth. The most interesting features of the formation are strongly in evidence along this exposed line of outcrop, for with amazing regularity we have proof of very frequent changes of the land surface.

From a coral sea to a high and dry land bearing dense vegetation, with intervening layers of shale and sandstone, and back again to the original sea is an interesting chapter in the geology of Northumberland. These beds of coal, with a chief characteristic of being imperfect and irregular, are found mixed through the ever-changing surface, and have been worked extensively in Northumberland.

Professor Lebour classifies these bands of limestone as seventeen in number, which goes to prove that on each of these occasions a large part of Northumberland was alternately sea and dry land.

Beginning at the top we have the Felltop Limestone, and in a somewhat regular descending order, i.e. Little Limestone, Great Limestone, Four Fathoms Limestone, Three Yards Limestone, Five Yards Limestone, Scar Limestone, Cockle Shell Limestone, Single Post Limestone, Tynebottom Limestone, Jew Limestone, Smiddy Limestone, Limestone, Robinson's Lime, Melmesby Scar Limestone, Limestone, Lowest Limestone.

Each respective panel of limestone has its corresponding seam of coal, and a brief **résumé of seams worked will be interesting,** at least to a generation now passing away, who hailed originally from these primitive mining villages scattered over the north-east portion of Northumberland.

Little Limestone is known as the Licker and Churm, the former worked chiefly near Lowick, and the latter in the Rothbury Forest district. Great Limestone Coal is also worked in the Lowick district. Shilbottle Seam, also worked at Newton, Framlington, etc., is below the Six Yards Limestone, known as "acre coal" at Shilbottle, and is the best quality found in the whole formation. Beadnell Coal is found in two seams below the Beadnell Limestone. The lowest of these seams, especially for this series, attains the remarkable thickness of six feet, and is known as the Eelwell Coal. The Oxford Limestone contains four seams, viz. the Swinhoe Coal, the Fleatham Coal, the Little Howgate Coal and the Upper Scremerston Main Coal, worked extensively in the North Sunderland district. The Dunston Coal found beneath the Dun Limestone contains three seams worked in the neighbourhood of Alnwick Moor, the principal of these being known as the Fawcett Coal. The Blackhill Seam or Scremerston Main (the "Craw Coal"),

together with the Hardy Coal and the Boulmer
Coal, are found below the Mellerby Scar
Limestone.   The Threequarter Seam, and
"Cooper's Eye Coal" are extensively worked
on Tweedside and at Eglingham, and these
seams, together with the Wester Coal are
found below the lowest limestone beds—
the lowest worked coal of the whole
series.

Before leaving the limestone formation it
will be necessary to give some proof of the
composition of these beds in order to assure
the sceptic that the geologist can fall back on
indisputable proofs for his theory by the
fossils found in the rocks.

In the lower limestones we have the coral
rock-forming animal which is to-day building
up islands in the Pacific Ocean.   A very fine
line divides the animal from the vegetable
kingdom, and the incrinites or stone lilies,
prominent in the lower limestone beds, are a
good example.   These consist of a pointed
stalk supporting a stony cup which contained
the animal, and good specimens of these can
be found near Howick.   The other principal
marine animals consist of the family of
mollusca, such as mussels and other bivalves
—*amonites*, *tribolites*, etc., and also the

whole family of *crustacea*—crabs, lobsters, shrimps, etc.

These shell-forming animals are the fossils found in the limestone proper, and the fossils found in the coal of this series are similar to the fossils found in the true coal measures.

Millstone Grit.—As periods of time moved slowly on, even the deep sea to the south got stilted, doubtless from the folding and warping of the earth's crust, and on the higher land a new formation known as the Millstone Grit was deposited over the sea bottom which had previously provided the Mountain Limestone. These rocks consist mainly of a coarse, gritty sandstone with intermediate layers of shale and coal. Some writers assert that the new deposit was carried down by Scandinavian rivers, the result of an enormous amount of denudation of the granite rocks in these northern regions. As these series extend northwards they frequently lose their chief characteristic and become fine-grained sandstone, but a good example is to be found in the valley of the Coquet near Warkworth.

The name Millstone Grit derived its name from the use of the rock for millstones in bygone days, when every village had its mill.

An interesting feature of this formation is that, like the limestone, thin, poor beds cf coal are found in it.   Here again North-umberland takes the credit for being the only district where this coal has been worked to any extent.   The seams, however, are seldom of any practical value, but in days gone by, being of easy access, cropping out in the valley of the Coquet from Warkworth to a little west of Felton, were worked at several places for local use.

Being at the base of the True Coal Measures, the Millstone Grit is known as the miners' farewell rock, yet the uninitiated frequently assert that there is plenty of coal farther down, in spite of all geological reasoning.

THE GANNISTER BEDS.—Immediately over-lying the Millstone Grit is another new order of thing, viz. the Gannister Beds—a sort of quortoize stilt or mass of gritty, unbedded sandstone, little known in the North of England.   Like the Limestone and Millstone Grit series it has thin seams of coal; and the seams so extensively worked on the seashore south of Amble are attributed to this foimation.   These rocks are mainly interesting as being the foundation on which rest the world's great wealth—the True Coal Measures.

THE TRUE COAL MEASURES.—The Coal Measures proper are, to most people, by far the most interesting feature in the science of geology, and here the amateur geologist can find indisputable proof which will convince even the incorrigible sceptic of the truth of geological reasoning.

As the surface of the land became elevated, climate conditions changed to a humid atmosphere suitable for the growth of vegetation. Extensive forests, chiefly tree-ferns, *lipododendrons*, *sigilaria*, and others, sprang up in profusion on the naturally prepared surface. For ages of untold time showers of spores and flowerless plants grew and decayed, and eventually formed a mass of decomposed vegetable matter. When a layer had thus accumulated to a considerable thickness the land slowly subsided, and the old forests were buried beneath deposits of mud and sand.

Compressed beneath these sediments, the decomposed vegetable matter underwent peculiar changes, brought about by pressure, heat, and water. From practical experiments it has been found that eight feet of this decayed matter is required to form one foot of coal. When the vegetable substance was exposed to the atmosphere the decaying matter went to form the soil, but when buried and exposed to the action of water and an increased temperature, it became converted into lignite or brown coal.

Besides, under these conditions, it gave off other gases while the carbon was retained. As proof of this contention we find Devonshire Peat to contain 54 per cent carbon, 5 per cent hydrogen, 28 per cent oxygen, 2 per cent nitrogen, .56 per cent sulphur, and .9 per cent ash, while Northumberland coal is made up of carbon 78 per cent, hydrogen 6 per cent, oxygen 10 per cent, nitrogen 2 per cent, sulphur 1 per cent and ash 1 per cent. Taking this reasoning a step further to the deeper deposits in South Wales, we find a still greater change, and anthracite gives the following analysis—carbon 90 per cent, hydrogen 3 per cent, oxygen 3 per cent, nitrogen ·83 per cent, sulphur ·91 per cent, and ash 1 per cent. When this is carried beyond the anthracite stage, grapite of almost pure carbon is produced. This is, of course, the composition of the solid coal, but during the plastic condition of the pulpy mass, gases were imprisoned and exist in cavities of the coal in a free state. The most notable of these are carbonic acid gas (CO_2) and light carburetted hydrogen (CH_4), the latter being best known to the miner as fire-damp.

After these seams of coal had been formed by submersion, the surface was again up-heaved, and another forest of vegetation grew and decayed on the new land, and thus the process of forming coal went on for a period which at best we can only conjecture. In the coal proper, no organic remains are dis-cernible, but in the overlying roof and in the underclay there is abundance of proof of its vegetable origin. It is an everyday occur-rence with miners to observe, spread out like a picture, beautiful impressions of the plant *sigilaria* on the shale roof of almost every coal seam, and very frequently a complete cast of the trunk of the tree passing into the roof above. Immediately under this cast, embedded in the underclay below the seam of coal, with careful observation, fossilised roots of the tree-ferns, etc., can be seen, and are known to the geologist as *stigmaria*. Early geologists believed the coal deposits to have drifted into their present positions, but the presence of the fossilised roots in the underclay disproves this theory.

The process of forming coal to many may

seem incredulous, yet we have positive, practical proof of these coal-forming jungles to-day, and to the promoters of the Cape to Cairo Railway, the coal-forming tropical swamps, with an extraordinary depth of decomposed vegetable matter, are a serious engineering difficulty to be reckoned with.

Originally these vegetable deposits covered enormous tracts of the earth's surface, but the folding and warping of the comparatively thin band elevated and submerged the surface to such an extent that on the higher levels the coal measures were denuded. In our own north country there are good examples of this destroying process in the Pennine Chain, which produced an anticline, and destroyed thousands of acres of this valuable asset.

Commencing in the North of England the famous chain passes practically in a straight line south, and its great elevation and its sloping sides was the means of considerably limiting the Great Northern Coal Field.

A cursory glance at a geological survey map reveals the fact that the great northern coal areas, Northumberland, Durham, and Yorkshire, are on the east of this upheaval, whilst on the west is Cumberland and Lancashire.

In our own locality a similar destroying process seems to have taken place, and we are forced to come to the conclusion that the great Newcastle Coal Field was not originally limited to its present northern boundary. From Amble to Berwick there still remains a considerable tract of flat country running parallel to the North Sea, on which there was doubtless deposited an extensive coal field. To-day we find that not only the Coal Measures are denuded but the Millstone Grit disappears a little beyond Warkworth; and even the whole of the Mountain Limestone formation is wasted away north of the Tweed.

For this extraordinary amount of denudation we might hazard an explanation. In the first place there is the Hauxley Fault, an upheaval of over one hundred fathoms, which seems to have been overlooked by earlier geologists. This elevation of the land surface on the north, with the gradually sloping uplands of the Cheviots, gives some proof that there would be an enormous amount of denudation during and after the coal-forming age, at least sufficient to place Amble beyond the border-line of the Great Northern Coal Field.

THE NEWCASTLE COAL FIELD.—Northumberland, famous in history, legend, and song is no less famous in the history of coal, as it is in the Northern Coal Field that we have the first authentic use of coal in Britain, viz. the traces found at Roman stations in Northumberland and Durham, and a brief description of what is universally known as the Newcastle Coal Field will be of some interest.

The exposed workable area extends roughly from the River Tees on the south to the River Coquet on the north, a distance of fifty miles; and its greatest width in the Tyne valley is twenty miles. Besides this exposed portion there is supposed to be one hundred and ten square miles under the North Sea, and two hundred and twenty square miles south of the Tees, buried beneath the newer formation, at present beyond the reach of man. A large tract in east Durham is overlaid by the Permian System, and at the junction of the Carboniferous and the new formation there is practically an underground lake. To penetrate this has taxed the rare genius, skill, and indomitable energy of the present-day mining engineers.

There are sixteen seams in this field, twelve

of which are worked, and with an aggregate of about fifty feet of coal.

Monkwearmouth is said to be at or near the axis of the basin, and northwards a great number of the seams disappear altogether. For instance the Hutton Seam at this colliery is struck at two hundred and eighty-five fathoms with all the seams on, while at Broomhill the Northumberland Main Seam which is said to be the same bed, is found at a depth of forty fathoms with only five workable seams. The great peculiarity of this field is that four distinct classes of coal are present, viz. household, steam, gas and coking coal.

THE PERMIAN SYSTEM.—The new formation alluded to comprises the Permian System, which overlies the Carboniferous. This is usually divided into two series—an upper and lower—consisting of new red sandstone, magnesium limestone, and chalk hills. As previously stated, there are no signs of these new rocks in the district, but a good view of the magnesium limestone can be obtained at Cullercoats, where it can be seen with a comparative thin edge; also on the seashore near Sunderland, where it presents a decidedly interesting geological study.

Of the other newer systems such as the

Triassic, Jurassic, Cretaceous, Tertiary and Post Tertiary Systems, there is no trace in the North of England, and as this is a sort of eyesight résumé, this part of geology will have to be passed over.

THE GLACIAL DRIFT

The present condition of the earth's surface is attributed to the glacial period, which levelled the rugged surface and eventually deposited the glacial drift well known in our own locality as boulder clay and sand.

The boulder clay takes its name from the stones found in it, and is simply the residue left by the melting ice of the last glacial period, which is explained by ages and ages of very low temperature, bringing about an enormous accumulation of snow and ice. Then a time came when the temperature again rose, and the mountains thus formed began to melt slowly, and consequently move in the track of the least resistance.

The north-east coast of Great Britain is all the more interesting, being the converging ground of two ice floes from opposite directions, viz. one from the regions of Scandinavia and the other from the west.

Like other scientific facts the man in the

street has no hesitation in giving the ice age theory a flat negative, and the reason of this is that he wilfully shuts his eyes to proofs staring him in the face. He will even go farther and demand proof, offhand, for the cause of these extraordinary mountains of ice which scraped, levelled, and put into its present shape, the surface of the land.

Scientists assign quite a variety of causes for this extraordinary period of ice and snow, such as astronomical changes in the solar system, changes in the eccentricity of the orbit of the earth, our planet. Others suggest that the solar system in its progress through space enters regions of very low temperature, also changes of level of land and sea, and a later theory is that the sun is a variable star. There is no general agreement on the real cause, but that it took place is strongly evident in our own immediate district.

On the shore to the south of Amble here and there masses of clay thickly studded with boulder stones can be seen in the sea banks. No better instance can be seen anywhere than at Bondicar, where the clay is thickly studded with boulders of various kinds, mostly limestone; and for many years the road metal for the country-side was provided by the boulders from Bondicar beach.

In Amble the boulder clay is, to a certain extent, wanting east of the burn, which passed over the site of the Station Hotel. Here the rock is exposed to the surface on one side, and on the other is the outcropping underclay of the Harbour Seam of coal. A little to the west, however, the thin edge of the boulder clay overlying the rock is found in the cellar of the Medd Memorial Schools. Immediately over the rock there is a bed of shingle and running sand, which contains an almost endless supply of water, and wells are sunk to depths varying from twelve to twenty feet, principally for gardening purposes. This was the chief source of supply previous to the introduction of the Hazon Water Scheme. A peculiar feature is the varying thickness of the clay over small areas; and a thin band of clay frequently gives place to a thick bed of dry sand.

South of the Hauxley Fault the boulder clay attains a great thickness, and at Broomhill Colliery in the sinking pit there were ten fathoms of very strong clay.

In the Birling Quarry, a little north of Warkworth, there is evidence galore of interesting specimens of glacial drift. Here you find ocular demonstration of the great ice age, and bedded in a thick layer of clay we find stones striated and polished, which are entirely foreign to this neighbourhood. From one common heap there can be produced, on examination, red sandstone from the neighbourhood of Berwick, porphyry from the distant Cheviots, and limestone boulders from anywhere beyond the outcrop on the northwest. But the most interesting feature of all is the limestone boulders of a purely Scandinavian origin.

A little farther north, near Hawkhill, the numerous mounds or hills are said to be the result of the opposing ice floes which joined forces in this part of England.

But anyone at all interested in this part of geology ought certainly pay a visit to Little Mill Limestone Quarry. Here large surfaces of the rock are bared of a thick bed of boulder clay, and underneath the clay the surface is found to be like the finest marble. This polished surface with the numberless striations are indisputable proof of a glacial period, and at once disarms the reasonable geological sceptic.

The last ice age, said to have taken place

some thousands of years ago, passed its enormous mass over the rocks and polished the surface of the limestone, while the rocks of harder substance, carried along by the ice floe, scratched or striated the polished surface sufficiently to prove the direction of the moving mountains of ice.

Besides, here is proof positive of the two ice floes having passed over the same surface of these rocks, leaving distinct and deliberate traces of the opposite directions of the moving masses. There is also evidence from the thick bed of boulder clay and sand and the numerous kaims or mounds to show that these deposits are the last act in the last stage of the glacial epoch.

LOCAL GEOLOGY

This brief elementary introduction to the main features of geology brings us to what comes under observation in our own vicinity. The seashore south of Amble Harbour is the happy hunting-ground of the local geologists, and here one finds himself in the geological chapter between the upper and lower Carboniferous periods. As is previously stated this is brought about by the six hundred feet rise Fault, to be seen on the seashore near Hauxley Head. Its course west is well known locally, owing to the coal having been worked up to the Fault at old Radcliffe, and the various mining ventures at Togston, besides the absence of all extensive mining operations beyond this line. On the south is the Great Newcastle Coal Field with the outcrop a little west of Broomhill passing southwards to the east of Chevington Station.

The old Radcliffe Colliery, sunk to the depth of eighty fathoms, struck six workable

seams known by the following names: the
Radcliffe Seam, twenty-three fathoms, a six-
feet seam of moderate quality.   Next in
descending order at thirty-seven fathoms is
the Albert Seam, five feet of grey coal, poor
quality.   The Queen Seam, fifty-six fathoms
—a seam in two parts—about three feet of
fine household coal with eighteen inches of
splint underneath.   Next is the Wonder
Seam, sixty-one fathoms, a thin seam of about
two feet four inches, of poor quality, not much
worked.   The Princess Seam, seventy-three
fathoms, a fine seam of good quality, ranging
from four feet six to five feet.   The lowest
worked seam is the Northumberland Main
Seam known as the " Duke " here, a thin
seam, just a little over two feet, one-half
having been split off by a band in the middle
of the seam, the whole ultimately running off
altogether a little to the east of the winning.
To the west the stone band gets thinner, and
eventually runs out, leaving a clean seam of
exceptionally good quality.   The new enterprise at Radcliffe " the Lady Newborough
Pit " is in every way similar, and was necessitated by a downthrow Fault of sixteen
fathoms on the south of the old colliery.   The
Main Seam was. not found in the sinking

shaft, but was struck by a drift to the west in two thin seams, the two portions eventually coming together as the band diminished, and is known locally as the " Double Duke."

Broomhill Colliery is minus the two top seams at Radcliffe but has all the other seams in good condition, and of first-class quality, especially the main seam, which is, or was, from five to six feet, of especially good steam coal, originally known as "best West Hartley." The Yard or Brockwell Seam is also extensively worked, and another thin seam is now being opened out by a drift, at a still greater depth.

The many mining operations at Togston have struck all these seams; the colliery near the railway having the seams almost in the same order as old Radcliffe. The three collieries form a triangle—Newborough, on the extreme east, ninety-six fathoms, Togston on the north, ninety fathoms, and Broomhill, on the west, is forty-five fathoms to the yard seam. The daily output for the two pits belonging to the Broomhill Collieries Limited is over 3000 tons, and Togston Colliery is laid in owing to a collapse in the shaft.

The extremity of the northern coal basin

is a little peculiar, a line east from Broomhill to old Radcliffe seems to be the axis. To the north the seams are abruptly thrown off by the Fault, and on the south and east the seams are gradually split off by stone bands putting in, in the middle of the seam. These stone bands taking the place of the coal brings about a large break in the coal area extending inland from Druridge to near Widdrington Colliery. On the western extremity of Broomhill Royalty the seams are continuous and of good quality by way of Bullocks Hall to Widdrington, where the entire width of the coal-producing area is about four hundred yards from the outcrop near the west end of the village to a little east of the colliery now laid in. Boring at intervals from this point to the sea, four miles distant, failed to find workable coal, even with a diamond borehole sunk to a depth of 270 fathoms on the Links near the Druridge Farm.

On the shore from Druridge Bay to Hauxley fishing village there is an extensive stretch of beautiful sand and a ridge of rocks known as Hadstone Scars and in places some fine examples of boulder clay with huge boulders of a very varied origin, for the most part limestone, scratched and polished on the journey hither.

A little north of Hauxley near the Great Fault is to be seen, when the tides are low, an interesting fossil forest where the trees of other days are fossilised *in situ*. Here also to the geologist is the most interesting bit of coast-line in the district, viz. a bed of shale enormously rich in fossil ferns, and other plants of the coal-forming age. From this bed and from Broomhill Pit Mr W. Walker obtained the following specimens.

Neuropteris heterophylla (fern). Sphenopheris obtulisoba (fern). Pecopteris (fern). Mariopteris muricata (fern). Calamite pennlyaria (roots of Calamite). Halonia regularis (the fruiting branch of a Lepidophloios). Trigoriocarpus patrinisoni (the seed of Alethopteris). Lepidodendron (decorticated). Lepidodendron stranbargea (leafy branch). Lepidostrobus (fruit of Lepidodendron). Artisea approximata (the pith cast of Cordaites). Segellaria. Giracanthus (Fish Spine). Fish Tooth. Magalichthys hibberti (Fish Scales). Anthracosia (Mussels). Udodendron. Cingularia typra (leafy form). Annularia brevifolia.

To the north of the Fault the rocks are

much distorted, eventually giving place to a
fine stretch of silvery sand. Near the edge
of the sand are the outcropping seams of coal
which lend considerable interest to this part
of the coast-line. The seam outcropping at
the salt pans has been extensively worked.
Another seam a little below this one has also
been extensively worked in the vicinity of
Amble harbour, and west to the outcrop near
the garden allotments.

These scrap seams are ascribed to the
Gannister Beds, whilst other thin seams cropping out on the banks of the Coquet are in
the Millstone Grit series. Near the White
House sands during the recent three shifts'
strike a fine bed of canal coal was accidentally
struck. The seam was of very good quality,
from two feet six inches to three feet thick,
with no underclay. From this we might assume that it was drift coal, lying as it is
between thin bands of blue shale, and the
specimens of fish bones found gave further
proof of its canal coal origin. It is estimated
that over a thousand tons of coal were taken
from this bed during the strike in the very
primitive manner of blasting the rock which
overlies it. Another curious feature is that
from where it was found it dipped dome-like

in all directions, and twice each day the in-
coming tide swept the whole mining operations and proved a very serious obstacle to
progress.

Nearing the harbour the lie of the rocks is
in the regular order with the rise to the north-
west. Two quarries near the shore supply a
good building stone from which the small
town has been built. There is a very distinct
difference between the nature of the stone in
these respective quarries, the Link Quarry
producing a very fine-grained stone; the
other, the Cliff Quarry, producing a very
coarse-grained stone famous for water
filters.

Near the salt pans there is a bed of peat in
the sand-bank about four feet thick. This is
a remnant of a dried-up bog which extended
inland by the Link Farm and the Hauxley
Fields to Hadstone Bog and continued eastwards to the south of Bondicar, where it can
still be seen in the sand-banks.

North of the harbour we find the outcrop of
the Millstone Grit; and a good instance of
this is to be seen in the Coquet, near where
the old granary stood, on the road to Warkworth. A thin seam of coal in this series can
be seen near the Beal Bank, and which has

been worked in the Houndean Burn at Warkworth and at Birling Carr Rocks.

Beyond Alnmouth Bay near to Foxton Hall we find the outcropping limestone previously alluded to as crossing Northumberland from Alston to Alnmouth. The limestone is of more than ordinary interest in the north and west of Northumberland, from the many and varied seams of coal outcropping here and there; besides, from time immemorial, mining operations of the most primitive kind have been carried on in this series.

To the north and west from Amble to Berwick all round the base of the Cheviot Range on almost every square mile there are traces of primitive mining to be seen everywhere; very frequently by means of drifts into a steep bank where a ravine exposes a thin layer of coal. But the great trouble seems to have been the steep gradient of the seam, in almost every case dipping south-east, and the enormous quantity of water in the overlying limestone made it practically impossible to continue over extended areas. Hence the frequency of what must have been disappointing ventures to the pioneers of mining in the limestone series in the North of England.

As some proof of the extraordinary dip of the limestone beds by an experimental bore-hole in the Green Lane, a mile west of Amble, the Shilbottle Seam was struck at a depth of three hundred and thirty-seven fathoms, while this same seam is found at Shilbottle, five miles distant to the north-west at a depth of fifty fathoms.

BOTANY

THERE are few more interesting rural studies than botany, which is becoming more popular with the advance of education. A knowledge of plant life was common to the Ancients, and Solomon spake of the "trees from Lebanon to the Hyssop that springs from the wall." The ancient Greek philosophers were also versed in plant lore whence was derived the medicinal properties of herbs. This, however, was only a crude knowledge, which ultimately became a science in the sixteenth century, and a knowledge of botany is now part of the curriculum of elementary schools.

It is not within the province of this volume to treat of the science of botany, and the sole reason for introducing this chapter is to lay before students of botany a carefully prepared list of plant life, etc., to be found in the district, by Mr George Waters, who is, without doubt, the best authority on this subject in the locality.

The following list is culled from the vicinity of the Black Bridge, Brotherwick Wood, Acklington Factory Woods, Amble Links, etc.

BOTANY

RANUNCULACEÆ

Thalictrum minus	Lesser Thalictrum
Anemone nemorosa	Wood Anemone
Ranunculus aquitala	Water Crowfoot
Ranunculus flammula	Lesser Spearwort
Ranunculus ficaris	Lesser Celandine
Ranunculus alris	Meadow Crowfoot
Ranunculus repens	Creeping Crowfoot
Ranunculus bulbosus	Bulbous Crowfoot
Ranunculus arvensis	Corn Crowfoot
Ranunculus scleratus	Celery-leaved Ranunculus
Caltha palustris	Marsh Marigold.

PAPAVERACEÆ

Papaver rhœs	Corn Poppy
Chelidonium majus	Common Celandine

FUMARIACEÆ

Fumaria officinalis	Common Fumitory

CRUCIFEREÆ

Barbarea vulgaris	Yellow Rocket
Nasturtium officinalis	Common Watercress
Arabis hirsuta	Hairy Rockcress
Cardamine amara	Large Bittercress
Cardamine pratense	Ladies Smock, Cuckoo Flower
Cardamine hirsuta	Hairy Bittercress

CRUCIFEREÆ—*continued*

Sisymbrium officinalis	Hedge Mustard
Alliaria officinalis	Garlic Mustard
Brassica Muralis	Sand Brassica
Brassica sinapis	Charlock
Brassica Campestris	Field Brassica
Cochlearia officinalis	Scurvy Grass
Draba verna	Whitlow Grass
Capsella bursa-pastoris	Shepherd's purse
Cakile maritima	Sea Rocket
Lepidium draba	Hoary Cress

RESEDACEÆ

Reseda luteola	Dyer's Rocket
Reseda lutea	Mignonette

VIOLACEÆ

Violo odorata	Sweet Violet
Viola canina	Dog Violet

POLYGALACEÆ

Polygala vulgaris	Milkwort

CAROPHYLLACEÆ

Lychnis vespertina	White Campion
Lychnis diurna	Red Campion
Lychnis githago	Corn Cockle
Lychnis los-cuculi	Ragged Robin
Silene inflata	Bladder Campion
Sagina procumbens	Pearlwort
Arenaria peploides	Sea Purslane
Arenaria serpyllifolia	Thyme-leaved Sandwort
Arenaria trinervis	Three-nerved Sandwort
Cerastium vulgatum	Mouse-ear Chickweed
Stellaria nemorum	Wood Starwort
Stellaria media	Chickweed
Stellaria graminea	Lesser Stitchwort
Stellaria holostea	Stitchwort
Stellaria aliginosa	Bog Starwort
Spergularia rubra	Sandspurry
Spergula arvensis	Corn Spurry

HYPERICINEÆ

Hypericum perforatum	St John's-Wort
Hypericum pulchrum	Slender Hypericum
Hypericum quadrangulum	Square-stalked Hypericum
Hypericum leisuhem	Hairy-stalked Hypericum

LINACEÆ

Linum catharticum	Purging Flax
Linum usitatissimum	Common Flax

MALVACEÆ

Malva rotundifolia	Dwarf Mallow
Malva sylvestris	Common Mallow
Malva moschata	Musk Mallow
Althœa officinalis	Marsh Mallow

GERANIACEÆ

Geranium sanguineum	Blood-red Cranesbill
Geranium sylvaticum	Wood Cranesbill
Geranium pratense	Meadow Cranesbill
Geranium Robertianum	Herb-Robert Cranesbill
Geranium lucidum	Shining Cranesbill
Geranium molle	Dove's foot Cranesbill
Geranium pusillum	Small flowered Cranesbill
Geranium dissectum	Cut-leaved Cranesbill
Erodium cicutarium	Erodium
Oxalis acetosella	Wood-sorrel

PAPILIONACEÆA

Ulex europœes	Furze
Sarothamnus seoparius	Broom
Ononis arvensis	Restharrow
Medicage lupulina	Black Medick Nonsuch
Trifolium incarnatum	Crimson Clover
Trifolium arvense	Hare's-foot Trefoil
Trifolium pratense	Red or Purple Clover
Trifolium medium	Zigzag Clover

PAPILIONACEÆA—continued

Trifolium repens	Dutch Clover
Trifolium procumbens	Hop Trefoil
Trifolium minus	Lesser Clover
Meliotus officinalis	Common Melilot
Meliotus alba	White Melilot
Lotus corniculatus	Bird's-foot Trefoil
Anthyllis vulneraria	Lady's fingers
Astragalus danicus	Purple Astragal
Vicia cracca	Tufted Vetch
Vicia hirsuta	Hairy Tare Vetch
Vicia sylvatica	Wood Vetch
Vicia sepium	Bush Vetch
Vicia sativa	Common Vetch
Lathyrus pratensis	Meadow Vetchling
Lathyrus macrorrhizus	Tuberous Pea

ROSACEÆ

Prunus spinosa	Blackthorn
Spiræa-ulmaria	Meadow Sweet
Geum urbanum	Avens, Herb-Robert
Geum rivale	Water Avens
Fragaria vesca	Strawberry
Potentilla reptans	Cinquefoil
Potentilla tormentilla	Tormentil
Potentilla anserina	Silver-weed
Alchemilla vulgaris	Lady's-mantle
Agrimonia lupatoria	Agrimony
Rosa rubiginosa	Sweetbriar
Rosa canina	Dog Rose
Rosa pimpinellifolia	Burnet Rose

ONAGRACEÆ

Epilobium angustifolium	Rose-bay Willow-herb
Epilobium hirsutum	Great Willow-herb
Epilobium montanum	Broad-leaved Willow-herb
Epilobium parviflorum	Hoary Willow-herb
Epilobium palustre	Marsh Epilobe
Circæa lutetiana	Enchanter's Nightshade
Circæa alpina	Alpine Circæa

BOTANY

CRASSULACEÆ

Sedum reflexum	Reflexed leaved Sedum

SAXIFRAGACEÆ

Saxifraga granulata	Meadow Saxifrage
Chrysosplenium opposit folium	Golden Saxifrage

UMBELLIFERÆ

Sanicula europæa	Sanicle
Ægopodium podagraria	Goutweed
Pimpinella saxifraga	Burnet Saxifrage
Œnanthe croeata	Hemlock Œnanthe
Æthusa cynapium	Fool's Parsley
Silaus pratensis	Pepper Saxifrage
Pastinaca sativa	Common Parsnip
Heracleum spondylium	Hogweed
Scandix pecten	Shepherd's Needle
Myrrhis odorata	Sweet Cicely
Chœ rophyllum temulum	Rough Chervil
Chœ rophyllum sylvestre	Wild Chervil
Caucalis anthriscus	Hedge Parsley
Daucus carota	Wild Carrot
Conium maculatum	Hemlock
Carium carvi	Carraway
Conopodium denudatum	Earthnut
Angelica sylvestris	Wild Angelica

CAPRIFOLIACEÆ

Adoxa moschatellina	Moscatel
Sambucus nigra	Elder
Viburnum opulus	Guelder Rose
Lonicera periclymenum	Woodbine

STELLATÆ

Galium cruciata	Crosswort
Galium verum	Ladies Bedstraw
Galium palustre	Marsh Galium
Galium aparine	Cleavers
Asperula odorata	Woodruff
Sherardia arvensis	Field Madder

VALERIANEÆ

Valeriana dioica	Marsh Valerian
Valeriana officinalis	Common Valerian

DIPSACEÆ

Scabiosa arvensis	Field Scabious

COMPOSITÆ

Eupatorium cannabinum	Hemp Agrimony
Aster tripolium	Sea Aster
Bellis perennis	Daisy
Chrysanthemum leucanthemum	Ox-Eye Daisy
Chrysanthemum segetum	Corn Marigold
Matricaria inodora	Scentless Mayweed
Achillea millefolium	Yarrow
Tanacetum vulgare	Tansy
Artemisia vulgaris	Mugwort
Artemisia absinthium	Wormwort
Tussilago farfara	Coltsfoot
Tussilago petasites	Butterbur
Senecio vulgaris	Groundsel
Senecio jacobæa	Ragwort
Senecio erucifolius	Narrow-leaved Senecio
Senecio aquaticus	Water Senecio
Senecio viscosus	Viscous Senecio
Doronicum pardalianches	Leopard's-bane
Arctium lappa	Burdock
Carduus marianus	Milk Thistle
Carduus arvensis	Creeping Thistle
Carduus nutans	Musk Thistle
Carduus palustris	Marsh Thistle
Carduus lanceolatus	Spear Thistle
Carduus crispus (acanthoides)	Wilted Thistle
Carduus acaulis	Dwarf Thistle
Carduus pycnocephalus	Slender Thistle

BOTANY

COMPOSITÆ—*continued*

Carlina vulgaris	Carline Thistle
Centaurea nigra	Knapweed
Centaurea scabiosa	Greater Centaurea
Centaurea cyanus	Bluebottle
Tragopogon pratensis	Goat's beard
Picris hieraciodes	Hawkweed Picris
Leontod on hispidus	Hawkbit
Hypochœris radicata	Cat's-ear
Sonchus arvensis	Corn Sowthistle
Sonchus oleraceus	Common Sowthistle
Taraxacum dens-leonis	Dandelion
Crepis virens	Smooth Crepis
Hieracium sabaudum	Savoy Hawkweed
Ci chorium intybus	Succory or Chicory
Lapsana communis	Nipplewort

CAMPANULACEÆ

Jasione montana	Sheep's-bit
Campanula latifolia	Giant Bell-flower
Campanula rotundifolia	Harebell

PRIMULACEÆ

Primula vulgaris	Primrose
Primula veris	Cowslip
Lysimachia nemorum	Yellow Pimpernel
Glaux maritima	Sea Milkwort
Anagallis arvensis	Scarlet Pimpernel

APOCYNACEÆ

Vinca major	Larger Periwinkle
Vinca minor	Lesser Periwinkle

GENTIANACEÆ

Erythræa centaurium	Centaury

POLEMONIACEÆ

Polemonium cœurleum	Jacob's ladder

CONVOLVULACEÆ

Convolvulus arvensis	Lesser Bindweed

P

BORAGINEÆ

Echium vulgare	Vipers Bugloss
Myosotis palustris	Forget-me-not
Myosotis arvensis	Field Myosote
Anchusæ sempervirens	Green Alkanet
Lycopsis arvensis	Small Bugloss
Symphytum officinale	Comfrey
Borago officinalis	Borage
Cynoglossum officinale	Hounds-tongue

SOLANACEÆ

Solanum dulcamara	Bittersweet

SCROPHULARINEÆ

Linaria cymbalaria	Ivy Toadflax
Scrophularia nodosa	Figwort
Scrophularia aquatica	Water Figwort
Mimulus luteus	Yellow Mimulus
Digitalis purpurea	Foxglove
Veronica officinalis	Speedwell
Veronica beccabunga	Brooklime
Veronica chamœdrys	Germander Speedwell
Veronica hederafolia	Ivy Speedwell
Veronica montana	Mountain Speedwell
Veronica arvensis	Wall Speedwell
Bartsia odontites	Red Bartsia
Euphrasia officinalis	Eyebright
Rhinanthus crista-galli	Common Rattle

LABIATÆ

Mentha aquatica	Water Mint
Mentha arvensis	Corn Mint
Origanum vulgare	Wild Narjorum
Thymus serpyllum	Wild Thyme
Calamintha clinopodium	Wild Basil
Nepeta glechoma	Ground Ivy
Prunella vulgaris	Self-heal
Stachys betonica	Betony
Stachys sylvatica	Hedge Woundwort

LABIATÆ—continued

Stachys palustris	Marsh Stachys
Galeopsis tetrahit	Hemp-nettle
Galeopsis Ladanum	Red Galeopsis
Ballota nigra	Black Horehound
Lamium amplexicaule	Henbit
Lamium purpureum	Red Dead-nettle
Lamium album	White Dead-nettle
Teucrium scorodonia	Wood-sage
Ajuga reptans	Bugle

PLUMBAGINEÆ

Armeria maritima	Thrift

PLANTAGINEÆ

Plantago major	Greater Plantain
Plantago media	Hoary Plantain
Plantago lanceolata	Ribwort Plantain
Plantago maritima	Sea Plantain
Plantago coronopus	Bucks-horn Plantain

CHENOPODIACEÆ

Salicornis herbacea	Marsh Samphire, Glass-wort
Suæda maritima	Herbaceous Suæda
Salsola kali	Prickly Saltwort
Chenopodium album	White Goosefoot
Attriplex hastata	
Attriplex portulacoides	Sea Purslane
Attriplex patula	Common Orache
Attriplex rosea	Frosted Orache

POLYGANACEÆ

Rumex aquaticus	Smooth-fruited Dock
Rumex crispus	Curled Dock
Rumex sanguineus	Red-veined Dock
Rumex acetosa	Sorrel Dock
Rumex acetosella	Sheep-sorrel Dock
Rumex hydrolapathum	Water Dock

POLYGANACEÆ—*continued*

Rumex conglomeratus	Clustered Dock
Polygonum aviculare	Knotgrass
Polygonum convolvulus	Bindweed
Polygonum amphibium	Amphibious Polygonum
Polygonum persicaria	Persicaria

EUPHORBIACEÆ

Euphorbia helioscopia	Sun Spurge
Euphorbia amygdaloides	Wood Spurge
Euphorbia peplus	Petty Spurge
Mercurialis perennis	Dog's Mercury
Buxus sempervirens	Box

URTICACEÆ

Urtica dioica	Nettle
Parietaria officinalis	Well Pellitory

TYPHACEÆ

Sparganium ramosum	Rur-reed

CALLITRICHINEÆ

Callitriche aquatica	Water Starwort

LEMNACEÆ

Lemna minor	Lesser Duckweed

NAIADEÆ

Potamogeton natans	Broad Pondweed
Potamogeton densus	Opposite Pondweed
Triglochin maritimum	Sea Arrow-grass

ALISMACEÆ

Alisma plantago	Water Plantain

ORCHIDACEÆ

Epipactis latifolia	Broad Epipactis
Listera ovata	Twayblade
Orchis mascula	Early Orchis
Orchis maculata	Spotted Orchis
Orchis latefolia	Marsh Orchis
Ophrys apifera	Bee Orchis

Irideæ

Iris pseudacorus   Yellow Flag

Lilaceæ

Ruscus aculeatus   Butchers Broom
Allium ursinum   Garlic
Agraphilis or scilia nutans Bluebell

Also Published by Sandhill Press

THE HISTORY OF NORTHUMBERLAND
by Cadwallader J. Bates.
A Sandhill Classic Reprint

IN AND AROUND - Alnwick...Morpeth...Rothbury...Warkworth
by Ian Smith
Ian explores Northumberland's towns, villages and their rivers.
Illus. with the author's own line drawings and maps.

THE LAST YEARS OF A FRONTIER
by D.L.W. Tough
A history of the Borders during the turbulent times of Elizabeth I.

MEDIEVAL CASTLES, TOWERS, PELES AND BASTLES OF NORTHUMBERLAND
by T.H. Rowland
A comprehensive guide to the many castles and Border strongholds
which form part of Northumbria's rich history.

MYTH AND MAGIC OF NORTHUMBRIA
Retold by Sandhill Press
Stories traditionally told around firesides, ballads sung by minstrels,
associated with well-known places in Northumbria, are retold here.

NORTHUMBERLAND PLACE NAMES: Goodwife Hot and others
by Godfrey Watson
How did a hill fortress come to be called 'Goodwife Hot' or a farm
'Pity Me'? Through these and other names of towns and villages,
farms and shepherds' huts, the fascinating history of
Northumberland is revealed.

NORTHUMBRIA IN PICTURES
by Beryl Sanderson
2nd. rev. edition of this souvenir guide containing 40 superb colour
photographs of one of England's finest counties.